To Karen: Bon Appetit !
maybe crepes at your next gathering
Susan Koefod

LET THEM EAT CRÊPES

stories featuring the French pancake

EDITED BY
MELISSA DOFFING AND SUSAN KOEFOD

Published by
Lulu.com
Raleigh, N.C.

Cover photo ©iStockphoto.com/dkgilbey

Portions of some of these stories, in slightly different forms, have
appeared in other publications. See PUBLICATION CREDITS, page 129.

ISBN 978-0-557-54433-2

ACKNOWLEDGEMENTS

We'd like to thank our wonderful contributors for their excellent essays and patience with this project. It's been a long time, but we think it's worth the wait.

A big thank you to Anika Fajardo for the countless hours she put in on the project. Thanks to Tim Curtis for his help with the design-related elements of the book and Emily King for her copyediting expertise. Thanks to J.P. Doffing and Mindframe for the endless advice and support. And, of course, thank you to Kurt Koefod for photographing us so beautifully.

Most of all, thank you, reader, for purchasing our book! We hope you enjoy it.

Bon Appétit!

INTRODUCTION

Romantic strolls down the Champs-Élysées. A quaint bistro and cups of *café au lait*. The Eiffel Tower and the Arc de Triomphe.

All of these things may come to mind when you think of crêpes. But the beloved French pancake is no longer limited to France. From the streets of Denver to the kitchens of Minnesota, from chain restaurants in Colombia to wharfs in Helsinki, crêpes provide comfort, nourishment, and a certain elusive, mouth-watering mystery.

You may chose to savor this collection a chapter at a time or devour it entirely in one sitting. Each tale is different, yet the crêpe ties them all together. Whether it serves as appetizer, entrée, side dish, or dessert—you won't want to miss a single bite.

If reading these stories leaves you inspired to travel the globe in search of your perfect crêpe experience, seek out a local crêpe café, or find a basic crêpe recipe and let your imagination guide your palette. However you choose to indulge, we hope you enjoy!

Melissa Doffing and Susan Koefod
Editors

TABLE OF CONTENTS

LA CRÊPERIE SAINT-MALO BY RACHEL GABRIEL

Just nineteen and hungry. We make love all afternoon until we are driven out of our hotel room in search of dinner, another bottle of wine, a stroll along the River Seine. It is your first time in Paris, my third, and I take you to La Crêperie Saint-Malo on the Rue du Montparnasse. This street is lined with crêperies, each vying for customers with sidewalk placards offering *le menu du jour—deux choix des crêpes, un pichet du cidre.*

We duck into Saint-Malo, its interior like that of an ancient, narrow tree. The restaurant is crowded with tourists and Parisians. From our wooden table, we can see the crêpe master standing over a row of hotplates, twisting a thin coat of batter around each with a rake-like tool. The place feels hand hewn with its rows of copper pots along the amber-colored walls and the pottery plates and cups our waiter places before us with a confident clatter. He is an anomaly among the old-world charm: a short bulldog of a man, bald and clad in leather pants. Him and the music. Michael Jackson's "Rock With You" spins around us with its disco beat.

We order—or rather I order for us—my French confident, having lived in Paris for almost four months. We've been apart for this long as well. I say each word slowly for you—*jambon, champignon, fromage*—you smile, following my mouth with your eyes.

My first crêpe was from a street vendor's cart along the Champs-Élysées and I found it doughy, too sweet, a sticky mess I tossed into the nearest trash bin. But at La Crêperie Saint-Malo, I fell in love with the crêpe's savory cousin, the galette. Made of buckwheat flour and filled with tangy Gruyère cheese, a slice of salty ham, and a layer of duxelles mushrooms, the primary flavor of a galette is nutty browned butter.

Our galettes arrive, their edges curling over the plates. They have been folded into a hexagon, the Saint-Malo's signature tribute to the geographic contour of La Belle France. See? It's France, I say, pointing to an oversized air bubble that could represent Paris. Thoughtful, you watch as my knife hovers over the galette, tracing the places we will one day visit: Here is Tours, there Le Mont St. Michel, Avignon, Arles, Dijon, Brest, Rennes and Reims and Rouen, Quimper, Paimpol, Fréjus, Strasbourg, and back again to Paris. Yes, you say. Yes. Over galettes, we affirm our future. Then we trade talk for forkfuls of this humble, hearty meal.

Our feet are in a jumble under the table. Our fingers take turns to meet between the crêpe plates before taking up knife and fork for another bite. We toast one another with palm-sized cups of cider. Its bittersweet bite brings out the flavor of our crêpes and the fact that you will be leaving tomorrow. But for now: To travel! To love! To life! *Vive la France!*

After the salad and more cider and two crêpes sucré with strawberries and chocolate, the waiter hands us our bill along with a lighter, its royal blue plastic stamped with an image of La Crêperie Saint-Malo. Later we will find a crowded café to sip our espresso, and you will use this lighter to ignite our cigarettes. Smoke and laughter will curl above us, then dissipate into the night air until we find ourselves alone again, standing on the Pont des Arts, our hands still braided together.

Do you remember how Notre Dame glows at night? The way the moon suspends itself over the great cathedral and how their reflections swell and shimmer in the ripple of the River Seine?

We will share this same moon after you have flown away. As we will—years later—share in the memory of youth when we light a pair of candles at our family dinner table with the lighter from La Crêperie Saint-Malo and celebrate our shared lifetime with a plate of homemade crêpes.

RACHEL GABRIEL lives in Minneapolis. A recent winner of the Loft Mentor Series in creative nonfiction, she is currently working on a memoir manuscript. She is the co-editor and a contributor to the essay collection My *Red Couch and Other Stories on Seeking a Feminist Faith* (The Pilgrim Press, 2005). She is an instructor at The Loft Literary Center where she teaches a class about food and storytelling.

EATING CRÊPES IN COLOMBIA BY ANIKA FAJARDO

In December of 1995, American Airlines Flight 965 from Miami to Colombia landed, not on Cali's runway, but nose-first in the mountains surrounding the city. Subsequent news reports placed the blame on pilot error. Exactly one week later, I kissed my mother good-bye and boarded the same flight, hoping for better navigation.

When I exited Cali's international terminal, Spanish bombarded me from all sides as people kissed, clapped, laughed, and cried. Relief that the plane had landed safely hung in the humid, sticky air. I stumbled down the ramp, out of the blinding fluorescent lights of the airport, and descended into the suffocating scent of tropical flowers. My wool sweater and heavy shoes were as constricting as the humid air. And then I heard my name. A shout in the crowd, faces that were eerily familiar like a dream that stays just beyond consciousness.

My father.

At age twenty, I was meeting him for the first time, the man with whom I share half my genes. The man responsible for my dark hair, my olive skin, perhaps even my ease with Spanish. And a stranger. He and his wife called to me from behind the cordoned-off walkway.

"Hello," he said, with strong emphasis on the "h" as if it would get away if he didn't catch it in his mouth. He had the same dark hair as me and his nose was mine. "My dear," said this man who was my father.
He took my hand in both of his—they were soft and warm and surprisingly small. He wasn't more than an inch taller than my five feet four inches, and standing in Doc Martens, my own brown eyes were level with his. I tried to reconcile this older man with the one in the black-and-white photos I had seen in my mother's albums. There were only a few pictures of him, often with a shirt unbuttoned halfway to his navel or a hat perched on his head at a rakish angle. He was still good looking, and I was glad to have inherited his strong, high cheekbones.

"Good morning," his wife said in an accent so thick I almost didn't understand her. It was eight in the evening. I smiled at her.

They each kissed me on the cheek, one of them grabbed my suitcase and the other my shoulder bag, leaving me empty-handed. My new stepmother eyed my baggy jeans and gray cardigan. In a tight T-shirt and short skirt, she was a striking contrast to my own mother. She looked about thirty-five—a good twenty years younger than both my parents—and she had shapely little legs, brown and smooth. Her dainty feet were in thong sandals, and her toenails were bright red.

Having grown up listening to my mother speak words of endearments— *mi'jita, niñacita*—in Spanish, the language had always come easily to me. In high school and college, I was frequently the star pupil with a flawless accent and large vocabulary. But Maria Cecilia's Colombian Spanish was incomprehensible. Every few words I recognized something: Family. Happy. Father.

They piled my luggage in a tiny silver Suzuki jeep that smelled like bananas and warm summer days. They urged me into the front seat, and Maria Cecilia got behind the wheel. My father sat in the back and leaned forward between the seats, hand on my shoulder, repeating my name over and over again, grinning.

***

She drove with one arm resting on the open window and the other gesticulating as she told stories. I pretended to listen and studied every sight as we sped past: young men on bicycles, turquoise and salmon buildings with clothes hanging from open windows, tiny cars speeding recklessly around roundabouts. A huge black woman in a colorful turban sold something out of a basket that rested between her ample knees. Later I learned that she was selling *chontaduros*, a small, hard fruit cooked with salt that I came to despise. Even though it was late in the evening, children, barely tall enough to peek inside the car, pestered us at every red light wanting to wash the windows or sell us bags of unfamiliar fruit.

Even at night the city was more alive than any Midwestern town. The signs along the roads were green just like at home, but the arrows showing the way looked slimmer and pointier. I recognized the stop signs with their red octagons, but they somehow seemed different, more vibrant and certainly more ignored. The cracks in the sidewalk were lush with green weeds and flowers. Back home it was the end of December, and there was nothing growing anywhere. Even the plants in my apartment were dying—or would be by the time I got back.

"*¿Qué quieres comer?*" asked my father. "What do you want to eat?"

I shrugged. I hardly knew what my options were. He and Maria Cecilia discussed, presumably, our choices.

"We're going to eat crêpes, my dear," he said to me finally in English. Crêpes?

***

I never really had a clear understanding of what, exactly, Colombian food was, but I was pretty sure it wasn't crêpes. When people heard I was half Colombian, they assumed I liked spicy foods, lumping all south-of-the-border fare together. But I'd never tolerated chilies, breaking out into a sweat around habaneros, poblanos, cayenne. The closest I came to Colombian food was the sweet *manjar blanco* my American mother and I would make for school reports about my birth country.

Maria Cecilia pulled into a dirt parking lot packed with tiny foreign cars and ancient Detroit iron. The walls of the restaurant were bright orange, and the tables were crowded. We walked past the diners out onto a cement patio. There were long wooden tables, and a menu was painted on the side of the building. White light bulbs swung from wires above us. "Angels We Have Heard on High" played through tinny loudspeakers.

"*¿Qué quieres?*" Maria Cecilia asked me slowly and carefully.

What did I want? I didn't even know where to begin. Mute, I shrugged again.

"My dear," said my father, taking my hand and pointing me toward the menu. "What do you want to eat? Crêpes?"

I nodded even though my stomach was still churning with nerves and airplane food and what I really wanted was something familiar, comforting, American.

The last time I had crêpes had been years ago. My mother used to make them out of buckwheat flour and fill them with broccoli, cream sauce, and cheese. I remember her rolling them up and placing them row by row into a glass baking pan, transforming a French delicacy into a Minnesota casserole.

"*Mi amor. ¿Qué tipo quieres?*" asked my father when a beautiful girl in thick mascara and pink eye shadow came to take our order. I studied the brightly colored menu. My textbook Spanish had not prepared me for a gastronomic vocabulary, but the words *fresa* and *crema* were illustrated with pictures of strawberries and pitchers of cream.

"*Crêpe con fresa,*" I enunciated. "*Por favor.*"

My father smiled proudly.

"*¿Te gusta?*" Maria Cecilia asked when our orders arrived. Did I like it?

The crêpe was filled with vanilla ice cream and a few plump, ripe strawberries and smothered in thick whipped cream called *nata*. The only relief from the tooth-aching sweetness was the delicate thin pancake. I nodded and smiled at the two strangers sitting opposite me.

As I washed down each bite with sips of warm Coke from a thick glass bottle, I thought about my mother's stories of black beans and tamales, salty *arepas* and deep bowls of *sancocho*. What would she say when I finally landed safely on the frozen tarmac and told her my first Colombian meal was crêpes?

ANIKA FAJARDO's work has appeared in various publications including *Minnetonka Review*, *Colere*, *The Talking Stick*, *Midway Journal*, and *Library Journal*. She was a winner of the Loft Literary Center's Mentor Series in creative nonfiction.

THE FLIP SIDE OF CRÊPES BY MARTHA L. LAVOUÉ

My husband is French, so you might think he would be a gifted cook. *Hélas, non.* Pierre has the appreciation of fine food bestowed upon the French and fully appreciates my efforts, usually giving me the thumbs-up compliment of *"c'est pas mauvais!"* (not bad!) or even *"je me suis regalé!"* (it's delicious!). On bad days, he speaks of how his mother used to make such-and-such a dish (*poule au pot* or *veau maringo*) when I have obviously failed his high standards. Over the years, he has learned to fry himself a *bifteck* or boil a pot of water and add (usually way too much) spaghetti. He can also peel potatoes and carrots much more deftly than I can, and I allow him to do this frequently.

Pierre's one talent in the kitchen is his ability to make crêpes.

His recipe is a family secret inherited from his mother. He makes them on days when I won't be home in time to make something else and he's tired of eating thrown-together salads or reheated leftovers. I can usually feel them coming. Or I might see the poorly dissimulated bowl of batter in the refrigerator. Like a good Frenchman, he allows the mixture to "rest" for a certain number of hours before being thrown into the hot crêpe pan. In any case, I can smell them before I walk in the door.

I prefer not to be there when he begins, since the first one is almost always *raté*—the crêpe pan too hot or not hot enough or the flour is not the right brand. This never fails to induce loud expletives (in French, *naturellement*) and threats to throw out the batter or to give all the crêpes to the dog. But once production gets going, the crêpes pile up on our large plate that is used almost exclusively for this purpose. He takes special delight in flipping them in the air and catching them in the pan, shaking the handle slightly to keep them from sticking. In 30 years, he has only missed the pan once, much to our dog's disappointment. He usually makes a dozen—or 13 for good luck. The last crêpe is for the dog, who watches intently during the whole process, keeping her drooling under control until the last one hits the floor. I usually start eating them before he's finished.

"Are they okay?" he always asks anxiously.

"Okay? No, they're fantastic!" I answer. I'm no fool, and besides, they are great—light, warm, melt-in-your-mouth crêpes, even plain, hot from the pan, sans melted chocolate, sugar, marmalade, or whatever else is available.

No, the only problem with Pierre's crêpes is that I've never learned to make them. Who could compete with such perfection? Thankfully, I am comfortable enough with my own talents to accept this missing link in my cook's repertoire and I plan to continue eating Pierre's crêpes to my heart's content until the end of my days.

MARTHA L. LAVOUÉ hails from California and has lived in a suburb of Paris, France, for forty years. She married a Frenchman she met while perfecting her French at the Sorbonne. She worked in IT but is now retired and devotes herself to her first loves: reading, writing, painting, and music.

DECRÊPITUDE BY MEREDITH ESCUDIER

I can still see the face of the crêpe vendor on the Boulevard St. Michel. He had a dour face on the sallow side with a vacant stare. All his customers got the look-through as if they were a bunch of bothersome phantoms flocking around his stand.

It was the seventies and my first time in Paris, where I was taking my first steps of independence. I would eventually end up living in the City of Light for more than 30 years, first as a young married woman in the fifteenth arrondissement between Vaugirard and Convention, then later as a young mother, just off of the Porte d'Orléans where my two baby boys would learn to walk in the Jardin Public. But at the time, at that first symbolic crêpe moment, I knew nothing of that. I lived in the immediate, with nothing more important on my mind than the pressing desire to acquire a crêpe.

I was not the only one crowding around the crêpe stand. There were others whose noses had brought them to this spot, whose stomachs growled at the mere prospect of a steaming hot crêpe folded in quarters and wrapped in wax paper, only to be hastily and hungrily consumed *sur place*. Having made my way through the congestion of street vendors hawking canvas bags, Eiffel Tower key chains, and Arc de Triomphe paperweights, I stood and studied with growing rapture the crêpe menu, printed on a chalkboard posted overhead. Its logic went from the simplest to the most extravagant, from plain sugar to sugar plus melted butter, through Nutella and dark chocolate (coconut optional), all the way to Grand Marnier.

I inched closer. From my vantage point, I could see the ladle as it emptied just the right amount of batter onto the hot, cast-iron griddle. Slowly the crêpe man spread the batter like a master plasterer. I watched and waited as the crêpe cooked, its lacy edges curling up as its color gradually changed from a creamy off-white to a spotted, golden brown.

"*Une crêpe au chocolat,*" I ventured, proud of my first French request and prouder in advance of the inevitable possession of the French language I would surely achieve over time. I looked forward to acquiring the nasal sounds, the lilting vowels, the throaty R.

"Yaplu," I heard the crêpe man say, addressing no one in particular. Was that a grunt, an imagined elocution, a dream?

I waited, patiently at first. Maybe the man's an artist, given to moods, passing whimsy, artisanal inspiration. Give him time, I thought, he'll get to me sooner or later. Except that he didn't. First he made a sugar crêpe and handed it off to my neighbor, then peeled off a second one and turned it over to another expectant customer. I'd been passed over, inexplicably.

Swallowing hard, I repeated: *"Une crêpe au chocolat,"* My voice sounded louder? Stronger? Plaintive? Desperate?

"I just told you," he said to me in exasperated French, "Yaplu."

Yaplu? What was he saying? Yaplu, yaplu. I mulled it over in my mind and then I got it: *Il n'y en a plus.*

There is no more. He's out, he's out of chocolate. He had just reduced five syllables of hard-won book-learned French into a two-syllable rebuff while simultaneously practicing the consummate art of customer disservice and depriving me of the chocolate crêpe I felt I so richly deserved.

I was stung. Okay, I was sensitive as well. I had invested too much into the moment. I had sort of hoped for a Jacques Tati drollery, a François

Truffaut moment of tenderness, a Louis Malle bit of irony. Instead, I was confronted by what seemed like puzzling reality (Jean-Luc Godard?) and it left me confused and forlorn. I found myself walking away, crêpeless, a lonely figure in black-and-white grainy footage, raising her collar against the wind, slinking off to the relative calm of the Cluny ruins nearby.

MEREDITH ESCUDIER's work has appeared in anthologies, literary journals, and the Meanwhile column of the *International Herald Tribune*. She has an ongoing column in a bilingual monthly journal, *Blablablah*. As she has lived in France for many years, her writing is often informed by the pleasures of the table. She is pleased to have published the essay "Watching Him Cook" in the premiere issue of *Alimentum*, "The Fig Lover" in *Culinate* and "A Man's Castle Is His Home" in *Imitation Fruit*. She is also a contributor in *Steeped in the World of Tea* (Interlink 2004).

A BUNCH OF THE BOYS WERE WHOOPING IT UP BY GARY ALLEN

It may not have been the Malemute Saloon, but it was freakin' cold in the small, snow-bound Catskill cabin. The boys had been indulging themselves most imprudently for hours. A sane and impartial observer would have reported that they were out of their gourds, babbling, helpless, drooling, giggle-locked stoners.

And that was before the munchies hit.

The cabin offered no instantly available foodstuff, and even the most rudimentary cooking was out of the question. It was miles to the nearest store, and the notion of driving anywhere was ruled out by meteorology and utter cognitive incapacity. Panic was threatening to kill the buzz when the head of the house—I use the term loosely—remembered that the cabin had a phone.

Today the boys could just order something for delivery, but back in the sixties there was no delivery, certainly not up in the mountains. Besides, any money the boys might have had had gone up in smoke hours ago.

No, they would have to call for help. A question loomed before them, a massive problem that challenged them just when their cumulative problem-solving abilities were, themselves, challenged.

Whom to call?

It had to be someone who could get there quickly, someone who would know what to do, someone who could be trusted not to turn them in to the cops (there was, you understand, a certain level of paranoia in the room). They left this seemingly impossible decision to the cabin's owner.

The boys had chosen their leader well.

Not only did he not fail them, he came up with a brilliant solution: the blond fifteen-year-old daughter of a neighbor.

"Ummmm ... Suzie?"

The others watched, waiting for him to acknowledge that there was someone on the other end of the line. They only noticed that they had been holding their breaths when he asked his second question.

"Suzie Creamcheese?"

The room exploded with feral laughter. He paused while the boys regained their composure (no need, of course, to frighten the young thing away).

"Ummmm … we have a little problem. Do you think you could come over and help us out?"

In retrospect, luring an innocent fifteen-year-old Scandinavian girl to a frozen cabin infested with three whacked-out college students might not have been entirely prudent. Luckily, for all concerned, it turned out to be the perfect solution.

She came right over, ignoring the blizzard outside, sized up the situation, and rummaged through the cabinets and refrigerator. "How about Swedish pancakes?"

In unison, the three lads collapsed in helpless anticipatory bliss, amazed at her ability to wrest divine order from a clearly chaotic situation. They stared, mesmerized, as her pale, floury hands formed incomprehensible arabesques through the air, air that gradually acquired a warm buttery perfume, a scent more intoxicating than anything else they had ever inhaled. One by one, tender crêpe-like pancakes materialized on their plates and, just as deftly, disappeared.

When Suzie left, an old cast-iron kettle was bubbling on the wood stove, two sleeping cats and three dozing young men were draped over various pieces of furniture, and bliss settled—as softly as snow in the dark woods—on the little cabin in the Catskills.

GARY ALLEN is the author (and/or editor) of: *The Resource Guide for Food Writers*; *The Herbalist in the Kitchen*; *The Business of Food: Encyclopedia of the Food and Drink Industries* (with Ken Albala); and *Human Cuisine* (with Ken Albala).

HOLY PANCAKES BY CATHERINE FLOWERS

Every Shrove Tuesday I make pancakes. It is an English tradition I observe even after thirty years of living in the United States. After all, English women have been making pancakes on this holy day since around the fifteenth century. It's part of our history, our culture.

Shrove Tuesday is the day when Christians are absolved of their sins and the last day of feasting before Ash Wednesday and the beginning of Lent. By making pancakes, those practical women of yore used up all the eggs, milk, and fats that were not allowed in the kitchen during the forty dark days of Lenten self-denial.

Yet I do not follow this tradition solely to honor my English heritage or to follow the dictates of religion. I make the pancakes because that is what my mother did. When I first lived in Wisconsin, making pancakes on Shrove Tuesday was an excuse for a trans-Atlantic phone call and some culinary coaching from my mother. Since her death in 1993, making pancakes on this day has become an important ritual of remembrance. As I gather and beat the ingredients together in my rural Wisconsin kitchen, I am able to travel back across ocean and time to a small brick house in Surrey and the 1950s kitchen of my childhood.

I can see my mother deliberately pouring the smooth batter into the smoking-hot pan; see her deftly swirling the pan and then tossing the pancake into the air and catching it in the pan before smoothly sliding it onto the waiting stack. Although my mother excelled at tossing pancakes in her own kitchen, she never entered the local Shrove Tuesday pancake race in town. Instead we would stand with her while excitedly cheering on our neighbor, Elsie Cooper. The women of the town, floral aprons wrapped over dresses, head scarves tied around heads, would maneuver the course between Stoke Church and the Town Hall, all while tossing pancakes. And laughing.

Legend has it that the pancake race originated in Olney, a village in Buckinghamshire. In 1445, a woman—clearly as dedicated as my mother to cooking the pancakes for her family—found herself late for the Shrove Tuesday confessional service. Upon hearing the church bell toll, she became so flummoxed that without thinking to either remove her apron or put down her frying pan, she raced to the church. To outsiders, it must seem bizarre that over five centuries women continue to honor the unknown housewife with a pancake race, but we English are blessed with many such seemingly crazy traditions.

Of course, the best part of the Shrove Tuesday was not the absolution of our sins, but actually eating the pancakes. Once my mother had tossed and slid a dozen or so into a pile, she would set about drizzling fresh lemon juice and sprinkling castor sugar onto each, and then arranging the rolled-up pancake on a large platter. I remember how the pancakes would melt in my mouth, leaving a sumptuously sweet yet tart aftertaste. I remember how in the blink of an eye my brother, father, and I would devour them while my mother remained in the kitchen working steadily on another stack.

Traditions, especially those associated with food, which involve the evocative senses of smell and taste, enable us to connect with our cultural heritage. But more importantly, they allow us to enter, albeit briefly, the door to relationships long vanished. When I read my mother's recipe, written in her fancy and oh-so-familiar handwriting, when I beat the ingredients into a batter, when I pour and swirl and toss, when I taste the comfortingly familiar flavor and texture of the pancakes, I am reunited for one precious day with my mother. Truly, they are holy pancakes.

CATHERINE FLOWERS is a graduate of St. Catherine University, where she currently works as a financial aid counselor. When not advising graduate students about their loans, she loves to write about food, family, and nature. Her hobbies include playing tennis and her conga drum. As an English major, it is a given that she loves to read.

THE REPEATABLE PLEASURE OF CRÊPES BY PHILIP KRUMMRICH

Most of the pleasures of eating are one-time-only, so widely varying from one occasion to the next as to be different experiences. The same dish prepared with the same ingredients according to the same recipe in the same kitchen by the same cook rarely tastes or feels quite the same. I could not say whether the crêpe somehow transcends this; all I know is that I somehow managed to have two identical and glorious crêpe-feasts a year apart.

My wife and I accepted an invitation to visit a friend who was conducting a study abroad program in Montpellier in the south of France. Although not one of the famous tourist destinations of the region, Montpellier has a peculiar charm. I could not tell you anything in particular that we did there, beyond eating and drinking and sitting on benches and ambling about, but if we did nothing, we went two years in a row to do the same nothing. It was enough.

Our favorite place was a tree-lined square around a delightful fountain in the middle of a long pedestrian avenue. One can while away hours just watching the changes in the spurt of the fountain and laying lazy bets on which unwary passersby will get soaked. Notable among the charms of this grin-provoking spot is a tiny restaurant, scarcely more than a long green awning over a dozen tiny silvery tables, called La Grange aux Crêpes. (As Vincent Price pointed out in his genial cookbook, everything sounds better in French. Try saying "Crêpe Barn" and see if you feel hungry.)

La Grange aux Crêpes is nothing more or less than a perfect crêperie. There may be other items on the menu, but with two dozen savory crêpes and another two dozen dessert crêpes to make choosing a delicious agony, who could order anything else?

The waitress—the same both years, down to the smallest details of hairstyle and casual garb—is a burst of Provençal sunshine, wherever she may hail from originally. She is the most beaming example of the humming, welcoming, life-loving French people who prove that the stereotypes are so much flapdoodle. She brings menus and drinks and leaves us to read. We read, sometimes silently, more often aloud; we moan at the very words, in gastronomic glory even before any food arrives at the table.

After long and leisurely explorations of the twenty-four choices, each of us selects a crêpe. Each of us selects the same crêpe both years, even though any of the other twenty-three might be even better. With five of us, we can at least sample five twenty-fourths of the offerings. She listens to our choices, and somehow makes each of us feel discerning, discriminating, devilishly clever. A few minutes flow by, as various as the fountain in the middle of the square, now flinging single sunlit arcs of water like cavorting dolphins, now in full symphonic spate.

She brings our crêpes. Mine are as simple as can be: little cubes of salt-gritty ham and a cushion of unctuous melted cheese inside crêpes so delicate, so evanescent, that they are more like aromas than solid food. I eat slowly, honoring every grain of wheat and drop of cream and crystal of salt and deep-red morsel of ham. But no matter how slowly I eat, and no matter how often I pause to wheedle a bite of another crêpe from one of the other four plates covering the tiny tabletop, all too soon my crêpe is gone. My stomach is far from full, but my taste buds are glowing.

All of us take a menu from the hands of that kindliest and loveliest and cheeriest of all waitresses; each of us writhes in the dulcet torment of selecting a dessert crêpe; once again, everyone orders the same thing both years. I choose a miracle of art and nature, crêpes with chestnut purée, so scrumptious that it hurts. Again we eat, slowly, slowly, but dessert is already gone. We linger for another half hour, light in our chairs, unfilled but satisfied.

There is no food like a crêpe. In my long and happy eating life, there have been a good many marvelous crêpes, but no crêpe-eating rhapsody to compare with those two identical two-stanza crêpe poems. We will not be going back to Montpellier this year, but other people will take our chairs and order our crêpes, or any of the twenty-four. The waitress will beam on them, as warmly egalitarian as the sun, and they will eat crêpes, or rather breathe them in. Lucky folks.

PHILIP KRUMMRICH has been teaching languages and literature at the college level for more than thirty years and has published translations, poetry, and travel writing. He has eaten crêpes and other good things on three continents and in fifteen countries and looks forward to doubling those numbers. He lives and works in Morehead, Kentucky.

SPANISH PANCAKES BY ERICA RIVERA

"I don't know what to feed you!" my host mother, a plump, jolly woman, exclaims on my first night in Spain. She crosses her arms over generous breasts and shakes her head of raven curls.

I am painfully out of place in the northwestern town of Leon. Like an adolescent Tinkerbell, my pixie-cut hair is white-hot blonde, and I am aspirin-pale and as thin as the spatula handle that my host mother waves in the air.

And, horror of all horrors, I am a vegetarian. My host mother knew this when she agreed to a month long visit, but the reality of a teenager who eats primarily pasta seems more daunting than she imagined.

"What is a meal if it doesn't include meat?" she asks as she raises her tired eyes toward the heavens.

Then her heavily lined brows shoot up. "You eat fish, no?"

I shake my head no.

She releases a full-body sigh.

Of all the places in the world to be a vegetarian, there is no worse than a coastal town known for its fresh seafood. My host mother flings open cupboard doors and slaps them shut with a series of muted thuds until she unearths a can of tomato sauce. She holds the can triumphantly in the air.

"You like spaghetti, yes?"

"Sure," I say in an unemotional monotone. I was instructed at my student orientation a few weeks before to be ultra-accommodating, to never refuse a food or activity. So, I slurp my plain spaghetti with a smile on my face, sure that as soon my jet-lag wears off, my host family will whisk me off to the town's best restaurant for sausage-free paella and fresh-fried tapas. Surely they will want to showcase the local food and accommodate my whims. *¿Sí?*

No. The next night we eat at home again. With twenty-four hours to plan, I'm confident my host mother has an extravagant surprise on the menu. She flutters around in the kitchen like a parakeet with clipped wings. I hear the bubble of water boiling and something sautéing on the stovetop.

My host mother emerges from a cloud of steam and sets down a plate before me.

Spaghetti. Again.

Night three: Spaghetti.

Night four: Spaghetti.

You get the idea.

Breakfast varies about as much as dinner—which is to say, not at all. Because I'm an early bird, my host mother leaves a big blue tin of Danish shortbread cookies for me on the table. Each morning, I eat entire stacks of the pretzel-shaped delights, sprinkled with hail-sized granules of sugar.

My daily walk to Spanish class is the only time I am unaccompanied, so I stock up on *almendrados*, an almond-and-chocolate-covered ice cream bar sold from vendors with bicycle carts. I drink gallons of *café con leche* and eat my weight in chocolate-covered croissants at the corner *panaderías*. I wonder how long it will take me to die from malnutrition.

One morning halfway through my stay, a sweet, doughy smell awakens me. I follow my nose to the dining room where a long curl of steam rises from a stack of pancakes. Deep clay bowls filled to the brim with strawberries, powdered sugar, and whipped cream are scattered on the table. There is no maple syrup in sight. I've never had pancakes without a generous drizzle of Mrs. Butterworth's before, but these pancakes—such a welcome change from shortbread—look so scrumptious that I'd have eaten them dry and day-old stale.

I sit in my usual chair before the feast, ecstatic to stuff myself with something other than spaghetti and cookies. My stomach growls a starvation symphony and urges me on. I lean over my plate and inhale the steam rising from the piping hot surface of the pancakes.

I slide my knife slowly, seductively, between each billowy layer. The butter dissolves into a lipid gloss across the surface. The powdered sugar falls from the serving spoon like snowflakes. My mouth fills with saliva, and my hands shake in anticipation of the first taste.

The first forkful is heavenly. The pancakes are thin and limp yet heavier than the Bisquick version I am accustomed to. Each wedge dissolves into a slippery, sugary goo on my tongue. Are these saturated in cream or simply undercooked? I wonder. Who cares—they're delicious. Another forkful follows. Another. Another. I am one-fourth of the way through the stack when my stuffed belly aches with satiety. How many pancakes does my host mother expect me to eat?

"¡*Dios mio*!" a voice squeals behind me. I turn, my mouth coated with powdered sugar. My host sister, a miniature version of her mother, giggles as she glances from the pancake stack to me. "Those crêpes were meant for all of us!"

Crêpes? I thought crêpes were a French specialty.

"These aren't pancakes?" I ask.

"No, *tonta*," she says, lifting up the layers with my fork. "Can't you see, silly? There are at least thirty here!"

When my host mother bursts into the room, she eyes the pancake stack, which now looks like Pac-Man. A smile flashes across her face.

"Now I know what to feed you!"

ERICA RIVERA is the author of *Insatiable: A Young Mother's Struggle with Anorexia* (Penguin Group, 2009). In addition to columns in the *Star Tribune* newspaper, her creative nonfiction writing was featured in LaChance Publishing's *Voices of Breast Cancer* anthology. Rivera recently launched maneaterbook.com, a website for foodies and infatuation junkies. She lives in Minnesota with her two daughters.

FIRST TRIP TO PARIS, WITH CRÊPES BY ERIC J. GUSTAFSON

Hundreds of faces—French faces—are queued up outside the glass, and the doors of the train hiss open. The Eurostar had been practically empty, but in with the rush of limbs and roll-on bags and voices comes a new traveler to fill up the space. Yes, the seats fill with butts, and the air fills with the furious and unmistakable smell of two hundred armpits. No, there is no mistaking it and no plausible excuse to be made here at Calais where I've barely breached the French border for the very first time. These people, I think, stink. Stink!

And we are all going to Paris.

A twenty-year-old guy slinks down next to me, drops a hard-clad tome by Kant onto his table. "KANT," it says, with a sturdy thud. I retreat to the window to avoid his furious black eyes and try to think this through, this first trip to France. I'm excited to be here, but at the moment things are touch and go.

On impulse, I pull from my jacket *The Stranger* by Albert Camus—a second-hand copy I found in London a few weeks earlier—and toss it casually onto my table. It does not make its presence known the way the Kant did. The guy glances briefly at my book but then withdraws a Discman and headphones from a sleek black case, disappearing into techno with crossed arms, and proceeds to ignore me.

I try hard to relax, to enjoy the ride, and to look forward to Paris.

I'm still a bit skittish as I loosen my legs and leave Gare du Nord. I attempt to dismiss any doubts and all the rubbish I've been told about France. Here, after all, are the summer Paris streets at the dinner hour, yes, even warm with fountain spray and chic pedestrians and street-side diners. And here is the Metropolitan with its lovely, curving signage. I gaze up at the letters, each lusty with nouveau flourish.

Then, as I board a subway car, on my heels are a plump, curly-haired man with a tambourine and a grizzled old tramp with an accordion. As the doors close and the carriage departs, the two surge into a joyful little number, and I'm as thrilled as the toddler bouncing on the mother's lap next to me who claps and gurgles at the music. What a beautiful evening in Paris in the spring of my happy life.

I find my hotel in lively Marais and then venture out at twilight. I follow the foot traffic and lovely smells until I find a walkup crêperie counter with a young guy wearing a yarmulke working the iron.

I step confidently forward and say, "Bone swaw; own crape cone-fih-TAR-ay, see voo play."

It is the first real exchange in French I've attempted in public—in France or anywhere. But my words cause the smiling crêpe man to stop smiling and then to squint. My chest tightens. And then I repeat my order, trying to breathe. By now the formerly smiling crêpe man looks downright confounded.

My thoughts race. Con-fi-TOOR? con-fi-too-RAY? con-FIH-tar?

The man turns to look at his own menu, to try to find the mistake I am making, and then he turns and smiles. "Con-fih-TWAH?"

"Ah, *oui oui*!," I spit, relieved and shaken.

We share a laugh, and he reaches to shake my hand. With a genuine smile he asks—in flawless English—what kind of jam I'd like on my crêpe.

Ah, *laissez-faire*! *C'est la vie*! First crêpes in Paris in the cool of the night when one is young!

ERIC J. GUSTAFSON is a community organizer and writer in Minneapolis, Minnesota. In between travels, his favorite local haunt is Midtown Market Crêpes at the Midtown Farmers Market.

THE MOTHER OF THEM ALL BY ROCHELLE MASS

When we moved into our first apartment in the summer of 1964, I couldn't cook. My new husband was a third-year student in dentistry, and, before we both knew it, I was pregnant. Morning sickness for the first three months took the edge off any attempt at cooking, but when it eased, we invited our good friends for brunch on Sunday.

"We'll serve pancakes," I said, although I didn't know anything about pancakes. Claire from next door told me to not overbeat the batter, stir quickly till the dry ingredients are just moistened.

"The batter will be lumpy," she said, "but that's okay. Then be sure the pan is the right temperature—check by sprinkling a few drops of water. They'll dance on the surface when the heat is right."

I followed her directions and learned to make uniform-sized pancakes by dipping into the batter with a measuring cup. But I didn't know when to turn them over and ran next door.

"Turn when the top is bubbly and a few of them have broken. And," she emphasized, "only turn once."

The first batch was a success, and I grew braver. From dollar size they grew to grapefruit size, floating in maple syrup, capped with whipped cream. My toppings gradually included sliced apples, cubed pears, grated chocolate, and my butter caramel sauce. I learned to add flavor to the batter. Cinnamon and orange was spicy and comforting, and it became a favorite. As I sprinkled Grand Marnier over strawberries, I knew I was on my way.

And then I was ready for crêpes. I imagined the fine, fragile crêpes I would curl over savory fillings as well as sweet delicacies.

Now I was on my own; Claire had moved away. I opened one cookbook after another and then found a basic French crêpe recipe.

Use a blender, it said. Process the flour, butter, sugar, eggs, and salt in a blender until the mixture is smooth. Add the milk one-third cup at a time, until the batter is a liquid consistency. Set batter aside for 20 minutes.

I poured all the ingredients into the blender, and while the batter set, I leaned over the recipe, reading the instructions out loud to be sure I understood. I dropped a little butter on the pan, poured a thin stream of batter over the surface, and tilted the pan. When bubbles started to form, I took my spatula, got under the crêpe, pulled it up, and tipped it over on a plate.

The six crêpes looked beautiful, curled at the edge like a crêpe must, and I was proud. I sliced an apple, rolled it inside the newly formed crêpe, placed a little sour cream on the side, and dusted it with powdered sugar.

Those first crêpes gave me the confidence and yearning for more. Our first Halloween, I surprised my husband and our friends with full, bulky pumpkin crêpes. Our first Passover, I found a recipe using matzo meal instead of flour. The Passover crêpes, filled with mushrooms and served with a tomato sauce, were a hit.

Now our oldest daughter has moved into a house with a big cherry tree in the back yard. We are planning pies and jams, but when the cherries ripen in May, I will also make crêpes with cherry sauce.

But while it is still winter, I think not of crêpes, but of my grandmother's buckwheat latkes. Learning to make her kreplach, knishes, mandelbroit, and even pickled tongue connects me with her. I'm doing more than collecting recipes; I am searching for connections, looking for what my grandmother knew.

In reading through her recipe, going through the same motions in the kitchen that she went through, I'm holding onto memories, opening the door to the life my Babba had and, surprisingly, making my own.

People around the world have their food memories, whether it's the African *injera*, the Spanish tortilla, the Indian *dosa*, or the Mexican *sope*. In Danish, *Pandekage*; in most German regions, it's *Pfannkuchen*; and in Dutch, it's *pannekoeken*. In Italy, crêpes are called *crespella*, and in Austro-Bavaria, *Palatschinken*. Whether with smoked salmon, ricotta, caviar, hazelnut-chocolate cream, cognac, or coleslaw like my Babba's latkes, these pancakes bring together family and history. And the French crêpe is definitely the mother of them all.

ROCHELLE MASS is Canadian born and has lived in Israel since 1973. Twice, she won first prize and honorable mentions in the Reuben Rose Poetry competition, and has twice been a Pushcart Prize nominee and twice shortlisted by the BBC for a radio play and Middle Eastern fiction. She has published poetry collections including *The Startled Land* (Wind River Press) and *Belmont Street* (Wind River Press), prose, pending publication.

BREAKFAST IN HELSINKI BY SUSAN KOEFOD

At Hostel Mekka at 9:00 a.m., the sun had already been up for five hours. Summer solstice was only a week away, and this close to the Arctic Circle, twilight merged with dawn in a near endless day. I had traveled from Minnesota to Finland to visit my then twenty-two-year-old son, Ryan, who was concluding a year of study abroad at the University of Helsinki. He now easily conversed in Finnish and blended in, having inherited his father's Norwegian genes: tall, thin, red-haired, and fair-skinned.

Years of exile from his life started before we could get the mother-son relationship down. He was not much beyond babyhood at the time of the divorce, and in an uncommon role-reversal, I was the breadwinner and his father was the primary caregiver. During our visitations, he was usually due home by bedtime, so instead of reading him a story, I was telling him it was time to go, gently coaxing him out from under my bed, and quietly buckling him into his car seat for the drive across town. We never knew a favorite bedtime story worn-out from endless readings, nor a comfy, overstuffed chair where I might have learned of his dreams or fears.

Those difficult days and years seemed endless, yet suddenly it was all behind us and here we were, a couple of strangers spending many hours together, thousands of miles from home.

He greeted me at last outside Hostel Mekka's iron gate. It was our last day together, so we planned to ride a ferry through Helsinki's eastern archipelago to Porvoo, one of Finland's oldest towns.

We'd have lunch there, but that was several hours from now. Ryan, a vegetarian, had been living in a land that subsisted almost entirely on mysterious fish stews and potato- and meat-filled pastries. We set off for the harbor, walking a few blocks to the Esplanade, a wide boulevard through the heart of Helsinki. The summer life of Finland took place entirely outdoors. The sidewalks were crowded with café tables and filled with the most gorgeous people in Europe. They were all vibrating with good health, as elegant as the artful Iittala vases and colorful Marimekko textiles on display in the shop windows along the Esplanade.

With the sidewalk cafés already crowded, Ryan suggested a place he knew at the open-air market on the quay. I glanced at my watch and realized we'd be lucky to get him anything in the time we had before the ferry departed.

As we headed across the cobblestone intersection and made our way to the market, we had to duck from the aggressive gulls overhead. One gull snatched a pastry out of an unsuspecting tourist's hand.

We came to the crêpe stand and found a table under striped tarp that offered some protection from the hungry gulls. Ryan ordered two crêpes from a beautiful teenage girl, and I handed over some euros.

With a practiced hand, she ladled batter onto two griddles and quickly spread it over each hot surface. There was an art to determining the correct amount of batter to create the wafer-thin pancake and then turning the fragile crêpe at just the right time.

Everywhere I turned I saw an endless supply of examples proving my own inferiority—my son who'd grown up tall, articulate, and at ease, even when thousands of miles from home. Nothing proved me more a failure as a mother than his ability to thrive without any effort on my part. I'd functioned as helplessly as a ghost limb in his life and now I was left with nothing but pain sensations in a missing part of myself.

While we waited for our crêpes, I looked across to the quay's edge and noticed a small crowd gathering and pointing down. One woman shouted in our direction to another onlooker.

I walked to the quay's edge.

In the water, a songbird thrashed. A small boat crept quietly up, its engine silent, the driver attempting to maneuver close enough to scoop the creature out with an oar. As I was doubly useless—non-Finnish speaking and netless—I returned to my son.

I glanced again in the direction of the crowd and then looked beyond it along the huge wharf of the Port of Helsinki to the cruise ship terminals. Here, cruise ships from all parts of Europe and beyond stopped on their way to and from places like Talinn, Estonia; Stockholm, Sweden; and other ports along the Baltic and Atlantic, even St. Petersburg, Russia.

The crêpe-maker was placing golden-yellow cloudberries on our crêpes. With a deft move, she folded them. I tasted the warm crêpe, still caught up in the drama a few feet away on the dock. I decided the bird was a baby, left too close to the edge of the water and abandoned by its parent. It floundered.

The cloudberries, fresh and seedy, tempered the sweetness of the thin pancake with a melding of flavors I didn't quite recognize at first. They captured the essence of the northern summer, combining the flavors of honey, oranges, and raisins. Tangy and lightly fermented, the flavor expressed the fleeting lushness of a Finnish summer. It satisfied a craving I didn't realize I had, so I relaxed for a moment and savored it.

When it was time, we made our way through the market to board the ferry. In moments, we were making our way through the busy seaport and out to the Finnish coastline, which bears a striking resemblance to the rocky ore-rich shoreline of Lake Superior in Minnesota. No wonder the Finns settled there when they came to the United States.

The familiar piney landscape dotted with lakes must have been a comfort to them then, a vision of what they'd left behind, just as the sight of the Finnish coastline, passing behind my son, comforted me now.

Ryan stretched out his long frame and leaned back against the railing, his short red hair ruffling in the sea breeze, and closed his eyes for a nap. As he slept, I was free to examine him more closely. Clouds passed overhead and cast shadows that transformed his face into versions I recognized in that traveler's photo album of my memory. In the flickering light, I saw flashes of the baby, toddler, and boy he had been and the adult he now was.

And then it came to me. Our relationship has most often been experienced in journeying with each other, just like now: sitting across from each other on hard ferry benches with the unusual taste of fresh cloudberry crêpes on our tongues.

I leaned against the cabin wall. For the remainder of the journey, I drifted in and out of sleep, certain that the bird we'd seen earlier had by now been rescued, reunited with its wayward parent.

SUSAN KOEFOD holds a holds a MFA in writing from Hamline University in St. Paul, Minnesota. Publishing credits include prose and poems, most recently in *Literary Bohemian*, *The Talking Stick*, *Minnetonka Review*, and June Cotner's bestselling anthologies.

MORE CRÊPES, PLEASE BY JENNY RUSINKO

"Unfortunately, there's fog over Paris and we cannot land. We are currently rerouting to Amsterdam where we will wait until the fog lifts."

The voice over the plane's loud speaker spoke in French, thus delaying my understanding until Madame passed along the English translation to the group. We had been traveling since early the previous morning, from Minneapolis to Detroit and then on to Paris, and it appeared that our travels were far from over.

We were a group of juniors and seniors with our high school teacher embarking on a French immersion experience, which would include a two-week homestay with a family in the Pyrenees region of southern France.

Due to the Parisian fog and six hours sitting on the Amsterdam tarmac, we missed our connecting flight and had to be bused from Paris to the small town of Lannemazen. At midnight, a frazzled Madame and twenty tired American teenagers emerged from the bus and were greeted by enthusiastic French families, ready to welcome us into their homes.

In my exhausted state, I clearly remember my first words to my French sister: "Do you speak English?"

"*Un peu*," she replied. Thus began my two weeks with the Chevalier family.

The Chevaliers lived in the country, about twenty minutes outside of Lannemazen. The landscape around their home was picturesque. Every morning when I opened the shutters of my dormer window, I was greeted by rolling hills, fenced pastures, and the peaks of the Pyrenees in the distance.

I appreciate the beautiful landscape now, in retrospect. But at the time, it simply provided the background for a more complicated experience. From the moment I woke up until I fell asleep at night, I spent all of my energy desperately trying to translate my questions, my needs, and even my thoughts into the most basic French. I was fully immersed in a foreign culture, yet handicapped by my inability to effectively communicate.

Therefore, when I think about France, it's not the Eiffel Tower or the Arc de Triomphe or the Louvre that first comes to mind. Eating the family pets; gorging on crêpes with Nutella; trying to deconstruct Led Zeppelin;

debating Coca-Cola's takeover of the world—these were my experiences of France. Yes, I will explain how we ate the family pets in a moment.

Since my time there, I have traveled the world from India to Africa to Central America. In all those places, I have had unique experiences, though always as a tourist, an outsider looking in. While in France, the Chevaliers allowed me to be an insider. Even though the language barrier created a state of constant confusion for all of us, for those two weeks, I was French.

Eating, breaking bread, sharing a meal—actions that cross cultural divides and language barriers, right? On my first morning with the Chevaliers, Isabelle and my three adorable little French brothers, Serge, Marcel, and Nicolas, took me on a tour to orient me to my new home. Kitchen, bathroom, living room, outside building, dog, cat, chicken coop, rabbit pen … We stopped at the rabbit pen, and Marcel carefully took out one of the rabbits for me to hold, all the time babbling away in French.

At the age of five, he had a hard time understanding that I couldn't understand him. Such a comfort it was, holding a rabbit and sharing the silent appreciation and love for a family pet with my French siblings.

The morning flew by as I explored the Chevalier home with my dictionary—nicknamed *"mon meilleur ami"* much to the amusement of my French brothers. My French mother called us in for lunch, and as I sat down, my heart dropped. A seventeen-year-old city girl from the Midwest, I had never developed a carnivorous palate. Give me a salad with some ranch dressing and I'm good to go. Chicken on the bone? T-bone steak? Deer, grouse, pheasant, or anything else that was recently shot in the Minnesota woods? No thanks.

When my real family did have roasted chicken for dinner, my dad picked the chosen white breast meat off the bone for me. So, when I saw what appeared to be roasted chicken on the table, I suddenly wished I had claimed to be a vegetarian before arriving. Even if my French father would have accommodated me by taking over my real father's role, I had no idea how to ask using my remedial French. *Mon meilleur ami* was useless.

No entry existed for, "Picking meat off a bone makes me want to vomit, but if you pick it off for me, that's okay."

"Le quel est?" I asked my French mother, referring to the roasted chicken.

"*Le lapin,*" she replied.

"*Le lapin?*" I questioned, crestfallen. I didn't need my trusty dictionary to translate that word. The roasted chicken was in fact the very same little rabbit I had so lovingly held that morning. I immediately decided to be more cautious about forming attachments with any living creature in the Chevalier household. I politely ate a small portion, explaining that I had "*un petit estomac.*"

The next day when the roasted chicken, complete with neck and head still intact, sat before me on the dinner table, my tiny stomach again came to my rescue. Yet, much to the confusion of my French family, *mon petit estomac* always had room for sugary yogurt, sweet crêpes, or French pastries at the end of the meal.

French pastries—yum. Being from the Midwest, I appreciated anything made with loads of butter and sugar. Every morning, I arrived at the high school with Isabelle and treated myself to a *petit pain au chocolate*—a buttery croissant filled with chocolate. And, every day after school, I sat at the family dinner table and filled up on crêpes with Nutella, anticipating the potential carcass that would later appear on the table.

On various afternoons, while I was stuffing myself full of crêpes, my French father would attempt to converse with me. I don't know who ended up more frustrated. I had less vocabulary than five-year-old Marcel, yet my French father tried to engage in adult-level conversation with me.

It turned out that he adored Led Zeppelin's "Stairway to Heaven," a song I knew but had never really paid much attention to. My French father wanted me to write down the lyrics. Easy enough—the song was in English. He then wanted me to explain what the song meant, in French. Impossible.

How could I critically analyze a song I barely knew and then translate those interpretations in a language I barely knew? I spent an afternoon repeatedly listening to "Stairway to Heaven," dutifully jotting down each and every word. As for the interpretation, I still have no idea who the lady is or why she's buying a stairway to heaven.

In retrospect, it makes me wonder why my French father obsessed over that song and its meaning. He probably told me, I just didn't understand. What I did understand was his aversion to Coca-Cola. Perhaps it was because I was an American in his home that he felt he needed to point out the absence of Coca-Cola. I hadn't inquired—I really tried not to overextend my exhausted brain by asking questions in French that had no relevance to my daily activities. When struggling to explain why I couldn't eat dinner yet could eat dessert, I didn't have time to notice that the family drank a generic brand of soda.

A lengthy, very one-sided conversation ensued over this very fact. I came away from the conversation understanding my French father's main point: He believed that through the distribution of Coca-Cola, the United States imposed our culture on the entire world, thus turning people away from their native cultures.

Had my French been more fluent, I might have had a rebuttal. But then again, I was seventeen. Before visiting France, I had only left the U.S. one other time, to travel to Bosnia-Herzegovina with my family. While there, I had thoroughly enjoyed numerous bottles of Coca-Cola and never thought twice about it.

Coca-Cola created a cultural tension for my French father, a tension that I didn't share. Yet, he loved Led Zeppelin, a very American band. Why was Led allowed in the house, but Coke given the cold shoulder? I guess my French father and I had more in common than we knew. We both picked and chose aspects of a different culture that we wanted to experience. I really wanted to eat French pastries, but not French meat.

He wanted to listen to American music, but not drink American beverages. That was fair enough.

My two weeks with the Chevaliers flew by, and I rejoined my group for a week of touring in Paris. Surrounded by English-speakers, I no longer struggled to communicate, but I also no longer felt immersed in French culture. I missed *mon meilleur ami* and my French family. Even though it was important to see the Mona Lisa, Winged Victory, Notre Dame, and the Champs-Élysées, they were, after all, just pieces of artwork and tourist attractions.

Everyone who visits France visits the Louvre and the other major sites. Yet I had experienced France in a way that no one else ever had or ever will. I ate the family pet; I survived two weeks on a diet consisting mainly of butter, sugar, and chocolate; I know all the words to "Stairway to Heaven"; and I lost my taste for Coca-Coca.

JENNY RUSINKO lives in Malibu, California, with her husband, daughter, and son. She works full time as a mom and part time as a freelance writer and adjunct professor of writing at Pepperdine University. She enjoys the beach and loves to travel.

CHOCOLATE-FILLED CRÊPE BY REBECCA EPSTEIN

One egg, one-fourth cup egg substitute, one cup 1 percent milk, pinch of salt, two tablespoons canola oil, flour, and chocolate.

These are the items you need to make the best crêpes in the world: my grandmother's. The crêpes I wake up to in Boca Raton, Florida, an exotic place with damp, bright sunlight and scratchy crab grass.

My grandmother's crêpes are sweet and mealy, chewy, gently browned. She fills them with jelly or warmed apples or banana slices or peanut butter or, best of all, broken bits of chocolate that melt in the warm cradle of the crêpe's skin.

Here is what I do: I fly down to Florida once or twice a year, since my grandparents are too old to visit me. I, who have lived in three states in three years, try to imagine what it is like to be confined to one place. So I fly down, and there they are, waiting for me outside the airport in their Taurus station wagon. The heat is like shower steam trapped in the bathroom. I am conscious of every inhalation, the air is that sticky.

"Welcome!" they say, and hug me hard, giving me wet kisses on each cheek. We go to their house in the senior living complex, and I go straight to sleep, still sedated from the Xanax I took before the plane took off. When I wake up the next morning, the reverberating clang of dishes in the tiled house, and especially the luscious smell of crêpes, plucks me from my dreams.

In my pajamas, I stumble muzzy-eyed to the kitchen where my grandfather is slicing bananas and my grandmother is leaning against the stove, a skillet in her hand.

"Hallo!" my grandfather says with his German accent.

"Beccale!" my grandmother says, overjoyed that I'm awake. "Good morning! Sit down, pour yourself some milk. Have a crêpe."

Get out an eight-inch nonstick skillet. Spray it with cooking spray. Turn the heat to medium-high. You'll know it's hot enough when, hovering your hand above the pan, you feel the warmth wafting up, just about threatening to sting your skin. Pour in a small amount of the mixture—you'll know the amount by sight—and swirl it around by tilting the pan this way and that.

Here is what I did when I was a little girl: Back then I lived on Long Island, and my grandparents lived forty minutes away in the Bronx. I stayed some weekends at their apartment, and in the mornings I took their breakfast orders on a paper pad like a waitress, and then my grandmother made the crêpes and I served them. She braided my hair while we waited for the filling to melt. The crêpes were chewy, soft, so sweet my tongue curled in on itself, delighted.

Watch the pan carefully. If you look closely, you can see steam rising up from the crêpe as it cooks. When it stops steaming, flip it over, but only for five seconds. Then it's ready. Slide it off the skillet and onto a plate.

Here is what I did when I was living in Arizona last year: My grandmother had heart bypass surgery. She was in the hospital for weeks with angina and infections and fevers and delirium. I couldn't visit her. I couldn't afford it, plus I was in the middle of school and teaching.

On the night before her surgery, I stayed awake, leaning forward, hands hovering, clutching at nothing. My heart pounded. I went to the kitchen. I got out the ingredients. I stayed up for hours making crêpes on my electric stove. I made savory crêpes with basil and parsley and a mushroom pâté filling. I made peanut butter and honey crêpes. I jogged to the twenty-four-hour gas station down the road and bought three slabs of chocolate. I made chocolate-filled crêpes. I made stacks and stacks of crêpes. I let them sit out on the kitchen counter and I waited. My dog stood on her hind legs, reaching with her snout, sniffing passionately at the counter, the crêpes just out of her reach.

When I knew my grandmother would be okay, I brought plates of crêpes to my neighbors but saved the chocolate ones for myself.

Break the chocolate up into small pieces and lay them out in a line down the center of the crêpe. Roll it up, place it in a nonstick jelly roll pan with all the other crêpes and cook the lot of them in the oven at four hundred degrees for ten minutes. This will get the crêpes to that fine line between chewy and crispy, and the innards will get extra melty.

Here is how I eat a crêpe: I take my fork and knife and slice the crêpe into bite-size pieces. Filling runs everywhere. I pick up a piece with my fork and slide it around on the plate, coating the pancake in melted chocolate. I eat it, bite by bite, eyes closed, thanking the god of grandmothers for giving me a good one.

REBECCA EPSTEIN recently graduated from the University of Arizona with an MFA in fiction and is now an MFA candidate in nonfiction at the University of Iowa. Her fiction and nonfiction have been published in journals such as *The Sycamore Review* and *Arts and Letters*.

TIN PANCAKES BY SASHA ASLANIAN

She called them "tin panacakes." Her American grandkids giggled about her Norwegian pronunciation but we'd dive for the platter piled with pancakes folded as neatly as handkerchiefs. Her *tynne pannekaker*, as they're called in Norway, were light brown with dapples from the frying pan, lightly sugared, and then folded into quarters. They were always served with at least three kinds of her homemade jam. Apricot, my favorite, was always on the table. This moveable feast could appear on the picnic table at our cabin, in her backyard in Seattle, or when she came to visit at our house in Minnesota.

When I went to Paris in college, I was surprised to see the French claiming thin pancakes as their own. I almost choked on the mealy whole-wheat savory crêpe; even the sweet ones with whipped cream were only carried by the wonderful ingredients on top. Though the street vendors' Nutella version was a decadent exception, I generally found French crêpes dull and floury. They lacked the springiness and suppleness of what my grandmother turned out in her frying pan: butter.

The essence of Norwegian cooking became clear to me as an adult. Most recipes—sweet or savory—use copious amounts of butter. Cookies, pannekaker, and cakes all follow the same formula: butter, sugar, eggs, and flour. Vary the amounts and you get different fare.

As I watched my mother and aunt take their turns at the frying pan with the long, thin spatula, they too turned out perfect stacks of folded pancakes. I was insulted when my mother gave my brother his own spatula and forgot about me, the big sister and rightful next-generation pancake maker.

"Oh, I thought you already had one!" she apologized, implying I already knew my way around a frying pan.

I confessed I had never made Grandmother's tin pancakes and didn't even have the recipe. When my mother gave me her copy, I distributed it that Christmas in my annual recipe collection.

My dad called me early one morning a few weeks later. "I'm just trying to figure out this baking part of the tin pancakes," he said.

"What baking?" I snapped. "They're fried."

Clearly my father was more hopeless in the kitchen than I was.

"Look at this recipe you gave us," he said with amusement.

I reached for the folder of recipes in my cookbook stand. To my horror, I saw that at the end of the recipe I had written, "Form into balls, dip in sugar and bake 8 minutes for soft cookies." The Molasses Crinkle recipe had been morphed onto the end of tin pancakes, wrecking both the recipe and my reputation.

I hadn't tested out the recipe and then I was too embarrassed to try. A few Christmases later, my sister-in-law gave me a boxed crêpe mix from Williams-Sonoma. I wrinkled my nose at the French imposter pancakes and reached for the tin pancake recipe, finally taking my place at the stove.

SASHA ASLANIAN is a reporter and documentary producer for Minnesota Public Radio. Her essays have appeared on National Public Radio and been published in *Adventure Cyclist Magazine*, *Modern Bride*, the *Star Tribune*, and *St. Paul Almanac*. In 2008, her words were pressed into cement as a sidewalk poem in St. Paul, where she lives with her husband and two daughters.

REVOLUTIONARY CRÊPES BY ALICE OWENS JOHNSON

I saw for myself in Paris how crêpes can start revolutions. My husband, my brother, and I were students there in the spring of 1968 during what is now called the third French Revolution, when students and workers nearly brought down DeGaulle's government. These kinds of uprisings weren't new to Paris. But 1968 was the year of revolt throughout the world: Students marched and rioted from Berkeley to Berlin to Tokyo. Throughout the world, students were protesting authority. The civil unrest was nowhere more evident or more threatening to the government than in Paris. On the first day of *les évènements*, the city suddenly exploded, catching the three of us American students completely by surprise. Cars blazed, set on fire by renegade French youths who also pulled up the cobblestones from the streets and threw them at the advancing police. To retaliate, the cops fired back with canisters of tear gas. The gas hung heavily in the streets, slinking into corners and snaking up into the windows of the sixth *arrondissement* where we were staying.

My brother and I had hurried to safety, scurrying up the winding wooden staircase seven steep stories to our garret. There we could observe the scene. From the window in our living room, we charted the battleground below. Our street, Rue de la Montaigne Ste. Geneviève, crossed Rue des Ecoles in such a way that it was perfectly situated for the students to set up blockades. We watched a group of banner-waving students marching down the street, which through the year wasn't so unusual.

Today, however, the group huddled at the narrow junction of our street and the Rue des Ecoles like a football team. They fanned out and gathered around an old Deux Chevaux, a two-horse-powered car that is like a baby buggy with a lawnmower engine. Then they began rocking the car. In no time, they pulled it to the middle of the intersection. In amazement, we watched as they lit the thing on fire, shouting and jumping as black smoke poured through the Latin Quarter. Soon, the sing-song sirens came from all directions and converged on our street. An onslaught of shielded police garbed in black spilled onto the street. During the battle, the police attacked the students with clubs and tear gas. Some were pulled into police vans. Many students had the advantage of knowing the unique topography of the labyrinthine Latin Quarter and were able to escape.

We Americans were unfamiliar with the warrens of streets, and although I was safe, when the streets cleared I waited and worried about my husband who would be coming home from the library soon. From afar we heard more sirens and bombs and saw black smoke unfurling in the spring sky. It was one of those bitter-cold days that showed no promise of flowers or blossoming trees. It seemed impossible that in a month Paris would be abloom with plants and trees that had opened, seemingly overnight, like umbrellas.

Just when we decided to venture forth to find my husband, he arrived home and shocked us with his account. "I was hit by tear gas," he said. "I started running with the other students to get away, then I slammed into a wall. I was lucky not to get arrested."

In a few days when tear gas entered our apartment, we learned it was impossible to close our eyes to the situation. They streamed with tears, and we could do nothing but suffer the torture with our eyes open. We never knew when the police (CRS) would come barreling down the street, jump out, and begin bashing everyone around. They were special goon squads brought in from the provinces, trained to battle upstart students, whom they hated. If we threw water from the window to disperse the tear gas below, the CRS were likely to storm up the steps, smash into our home, and take us away in cuffs. And God help the students, especially the Americans, who were suddenly diplomatically on their own if they got into trouble with the French government.

The students' energy and brashness during that first week lulled us into thinking the riots would end soon, and the students would rise victorious. All along the narrow streets that led to the market, bold graffiti depicted the goon squads yielding their batons, clubbing innocent students. The public sentiment definitely sided with the youth. The movement strengthened, the students gathered more power by garnering favor with the workers. Even such luminaries as actor Jean-Louis Barrault signed on, giving the students the run of the Odéon theater. *Liberté, fraternité, egalité* was written in black ink partout, especially down in the tiled walls of the metros. But metros weren't safe havens as a crowd discovered when the police shut the gates and crushed the escapees looking for a way out.

With each takeover, the students got headier with their power. Soon they began manufacturing and tossing Molotov cocktails in earnest off the steep roofs. The sound was deafening and had a deep charge to it, though it was impossible to imagine such a thundering explosion could come from a wine bottled filled with gasoline.

We had a ringside seat for pitched battles that went on for nearly two months. I remember seeing youthful cat-burglar-like silhouettes as they scampered from one Mansard roof to another. Backlit against the Parisian sky, it seemed that the drama and characters from a nineteenth-century novel like *Les Miserables* had come to life. When the garbage workers joined in on the strikes, another lethal smell punctuated the air. The stench of mounting trash climbed clear up to the third floor of our sixteenth-century apartment building.

During those trying weeks, I had to give up my courses at Alliance Francaise. When the police patrolled the streets where students were likely to gather and began forcing young girls into their vans, it was no longer safe to cross through the tranquil Luxembourg Gardens. Soon after that, the classes were shut down. But staying at home was not helping me feel calm. My nerves frayed as I jumped at each explosion and even learned how to calculate how far away the battle was simply by listening to the distant detonations. Because I desperately needed a distraction from the boredom and the anxiety, I signed up for a cooking course at a school called Ecole Menagère not far from home.

I had high hopes as the first day of class arrived and fully expected I'd find a fancy kitchen with copper pots dangling and fresh blue aprons for all. Instead, I arrived at a sunken kitchen with the school's name freshly chalked on a board like the menus outside cafés and restaurants. Inside the dark recesses of someone's home, I found myself among young French girls who had chosen the path of French home economics. While other well-dressed intellectual young women were sucking on Gaulois cigarettes and writing pithy notes in cafés, ink staining their fingers, these girls wanted to find a way to their husbands' hearts through cuisine.

And Madame la chef had little patience with my stumbling French. I learned how stingy the French can be about sharing their language. No sweet corrections when the wrong verb is used, it's *"faute, Mademoiselle."* Period. Add to the language barrier the difference in measurements. Cups, teaspoons? *"Mais non, Mademoiselle."* I kept telling her I was a madame, hoping to gain a little respect. As the bombs went off, I was determined to keep my composure, to show these demoiselles the unflinching character of an American. I would conquer the daunting preparation: how to make a *véritable crêpe*.

The French spare no expense in kitchen equipment. They may keep their heat registers set at fifty, use scrub cloths and tea towels from World War II, but if you want to make a crêpe, of course you need a pan for that and only that purpose. Madame Chef even had certain wrist movements to accompany the flipping of the crêpe, something that might be taught in tennis instruction. And so we practiced our flipping techniques as if we were going on stage, all silent and grim. My wrist felt stiff in that cold room where I could often see my breath. I wish I could have worn my gloves, but knew Madame would protest.

After several hours of wrist training, we got to the main event. The thing I remember most about the preparation of the pan for crêpes was the use of gauze to smear the oily pan *précisément*, nothing wasted in this class, *mais non*. I remember Madame searching about for gauze and I wondered if she might offer up her old stained shirts for this swiping.

"Ooh, m'enfin," she said, as she searched the deep, dark drawers for something to substitute for the gauze. I stepped backwards, sure there were mice in there. Then she disappeared behind the curtains that hid the freezing bathroom. I was corrected many times when I asked for directions to a bathroom. That was where one took a bath, I was told. A water closet, on the other hand, has only one function.

In a moment, she returned. Something was bulging in her apron pocket. My first guess was that she'd balled up toilet paper for us to use. My second guess was gauze bandages she'd ripped off the back of one of the student ambulances. But no, she was much more inventive.

"Voilà," she said, brandishing the French equivalent of a Kotex pad. Thankfully, it was unused. Was I the only one who was slightly appalled by this ad hoc kitchen *accoutrement*?

And so the crêpe lesson became a two-day event with the flipping, the swiping, and the precise mixing of eggs, flour, and milk. No Julia Child fun in this place as the butter turned the Kotex pad into a lovely brown color.

Like pancakes, crêpes have to be slightly bubbly before they are flipped. Madame taught us to agitate the pan so the precious crêpe did not stick. As performance time neared, I wondered if I could I flip my crêpe as well as my kitchen comrades. I agitated my pan as I'd been instructed, hitting the side of the pan with my other wrist so it didn't stick. Never mind the pain, it was my all for art.

Most likely my class act would have been more professional had it not been interrupted by the loud explosion of a bomb just outside in the street, a blast that should have taken out our windows. I was so shaken by the proximity, my crêpe fell on the floor, burnt on one side and soggy on the other.

"*Oh, la la,*" Madam said sadly as if one of her students had fallen in the trenches. Such a waste of flour, milk, and egg.

And so I left the class crêpeless but craving that sweet thin pancake, smeared with raspberry jelly, swirling in my mouth. I took the long way home through the market area called the Mouffetard where crêpes cook on outdoor pans, spread perfectly by a spatula, rolled like fine Cuban cigars.

On the street corner at the top of the market, I watched a woman wrapped in a shawl, a scarf on her head, as she effortlessly poured and spread the dessert across two large pans, perhaps fourteen inches in diameter. Her stoves were two large barrels, the kind homeless folks use for warmth.

"*Un crêpe, s'il vous plait, Madame,*" I said.

"*Mais non, Mademoiselle. C'est UNE crêpe.*"

As I had just finished nearly hours grappling with the coveted crêpe, I felt confident in my choice of *un* versus *une*.

"*Vous êtes trompé, Mademoiselle.*" She held the crêpe back. It was clear she would not sell this until I called it by its proper name. "*Voila, UNE crêpe.*"

The normal street camaraderie I'd experienced in the fall and winter was now laced with contention. Street fighting was chewing up the psyches of those who had lost sales because of the students taking over their territory. Barricades outside the city had halted many fruit and vegetable trucks. Some of the stalls, once overflowing with bounty, were now empty. The shopkeepers were ready for conflict.

The battle of the crêpe escalated as a small group gathered, huddling close to the warm fire. No American was going to get the best of her knowledge of the definite article. And now she had an audience. It was going to be a Punch and Judy affair. And so as the crêpe got colder, we disputed the correctness of this foolish grammatical error I had made. It felt like a tribunal or perhaps one of those disputes on the correctness of a word decided in the Supreme Court of diction known as Academie Francaise.

A man with glass windows strapped to his back threw in his two cents, explaining that he'd lived in the Mouffetard all his life, eaten these crêpes daily, sometimes with cognac for breakfast, and was *absolutement certain* that Madame was correct. I was afraid he'd turn in anger and slice me with the sharp glass edges he carried.

This struggle became the battle between the *uns* and the *unes*, each contributor holding forth on how they knew *certainment* that they were correct. One woman with her big pearl earrings and the obligatory

Hermes scarf added: *"Un crêpe est tissue. Une crêpe est la dessert. J'en suis sur."* She then about-faced, a baguette tucked under her arm, and, with the stature of a little Napoleon, marched down the steep street.

As this dispute wore on, my attention wandered. All I wanted was a crêpe. A hot crêpe filled with raspberry jam, drenched in butter. Was that so much to ask? Then I noticed for the first time since the revolution the first buds of May bulging against a splintered cosmos. Off in the distance, explosions popped and smoked, filling the Parisian skyline. Ultimately, I retreated in defeat. I could not dissuade the crêpe lady about the correct use of une. I bought it anyway.

That robin's egg blue afternoon, the Latin Quarter trailed with necking couples as I wound through the meandering streets home. Suddenly, it seemed they'd forgotten the revolution; their hearts had turned to love and spring in Paris. By the time I ate my crêpe, it was cold and soggy. I was sure I could make one better than that.

ALICE OWENS JOHNSON grew up in New Orleans and has lived in France, England, Italy, and Mexico. Her work has been published in the following anthologies: *O. Henry Collection of Short Stories, I Thought My Father Was God,* edited by Paul Auster, and *Alice Redux: Stories about Alice in Wonderland and Lewis Carroll.* "Saturday's Child" won first prize and was published by the literary magazine *The Crucible.* In addition she won first prize in the Tennessee Writer's Alliance for her short story "A Soft Tread." It is published in the online magazine *Maypop.* Her work has also appeared in *The Lyricist, Pembroke Magazine* and *The Guilford Review.* Most recently she received Honorable Mention and publication in *Kakalak: anthology of Carolina Poets.* Her poem "Gumbo" now appears in the anthology, *The Sound of Poets Cooking,* proceeds to benefit the homeless.

ONE TRADITION BY SHANE ALAN NOECKER

Though I was baptized into the Catholic faith as a baby, the only time I attended Mass, after age five, was on Christmas Eve when I went with my extended family on my dad's side—minus my dad, who stayed at my aunt's house to watch for reindeer. And even though Santa always came to our house around four thirty in the afternoon and left our presents under the tree while we were inside Mary Mother of the Church Catholic church, my dad never once caught a glimpse of him.

Mass was exciting. Because I was anticipating presents—what would I get? Tetris for the NES? Snake Mountain playset? Because I was sitting in the same pew as the cousins I rarely saw. Because tomorrow I'd get to eat a Christmas morning breakfast of crêpes and caramel rolls. Because there were all these strange once-a-year sensations—hearing the reverberation of whispers in the wide, dim, cave-like sanctuary; smelling the pine garlands climbing up the brick support pillars; feeling the masses of cold air let in with the late parishioners.

Once the pews were packed with bodies and as people snuck in late through the back, the stone room warmed. There was no room to get my coat off, and I grew hotter and hotter, never sweating, but feeling certain I might faint. As the nervous nugget in my stomach grew and those around me started responding to the priest's mellifluous cries with songs I didn't know, I felt as though I might leave my body.

Usually, during Communion at the end of the Mass, I would file out with my mom and siblings and wait at the back of the church for Grammie and Grandpa to walk with us to the cars to beat the rush out of the parking lot. But one year—maybe I'd ridden with my uncle, I don't know—as the Communion lines formed, I lost sight of my mom in all the multicolored pea coats and ski jackets. I planned to just stay in my seat as my uncle, aunt, and cousins went forward for the host, but Uncle Tom said, "Come on, Shane. Get in line."

I stood behind my cousin. Did my uncle mean for me to take Communion? Though I couldn't have been older than nine or ten, I knew that it was a sin for non-Catholics to partake of the transubstantiated wafers. Maybe my uncle had forgotten that we were Baptists now. I wasn't afraid to eat one of the perfect paper-thin circles. The sweater-wearing layman at the front of the line was only handing out crackers. Like my dad, I didn't believe in the power of the Catholic Church to transform unleavened bread into human flesh.

But what if there was a reason not to eat the wafers? If nothing else, it was probably bad luck. And maybe transubstantiation didn't change the chemical make-up of the bread but put a curse on it that would cause a horrible stomach ache if you weren't Catholic? Or, even worse, what if partaking of Catholic Communion was the unforgivable sin that Jesus had spoken of, the blasphemy of the Holy Ghost, and by eating it I would somehow negate the eternal salvation gained when I'd prayed for salvation at summer camp?

By the time I got up to the layman doling out wafers, I was almost in tears.

"Body of Christ," the bearded layman said.

"I —"

He repeated the words more insistently. "Body of Christ."

I turned and ran down the aisle toward the daylit doors and out into the wintry parking lot. My mouth was empty. Perhaps I would be saved.

The reason I didn't usually go to Mass, though I had been baptized Catholic, was because my father had been born again when he was thirty-three years old, the same age Jesus had been when he walked up Calvary Hill. Every Sunday, my dad drove my siblings and me up a road running parallel to the Mississippi to a small, independent, fundamentalist Baptist church.

As Baptists, we weren't required to go to church like my Catholic relatives who were supposed to go either Christmas Eve or Christmas Day and every Sunday. We went to church because we wanted to. Like my dad, I believed that being a Baptist meant being more authentic, less automatic.

We didn't sing the same songs and repeat the same prayers every service. Those of us who had been saved, as I had been at Bible camp the year I was seven, had the Holy Spirit living within us, which wasn't to say that we spoke gibberish and danced around like Pentecostals but that we were genuine, we prayed what was in our hearts. Our prayers were different every Sunday.

As fundamentalists, we had no respect for tradition—in our midst or anyone else's. Our pastor preached against the empty rituals of the Anglicans, the Catholics and the Jews. One Sunday, he said—from the pulpit—that he didn't see why people were so sad about the dynamiting of the fourteen-hundred-year-old giant statues of Buddha in Bamyan, Afghanistan. These were, after all, idols, just as the fundamentalist Muslim government had said.

As Baptists we had only two sacraments: Communion and baptism. These were the only two that were directly based on scripture and not tradition. Baptism was a full immersion in a river, lake, ocean, swimming pool, hot tub, or tank hidden beneath the floor of the dais at the front of our sanctuary. And because it was a one-off, like birth or death, there was no danger of it becoming rote.

Communion, on the other hand, was something done in remembrance of Jesus, something repeated often, so it was always in danger of losing its meaning and becoming ritual. As if to combat this, the one-hundred-member church we attended only doled out Communion once a month during a Sunday evening service.

In a reverse of the offering collection, the deacons passed around silver plates with the tiniest, most tasteless crackers, followed by little, wide-mouthed plastic shot glasses of grape juice. The pastor read one of the Last Supper passages from the Gospels and then we ate in unison, chewing with our eyes downturned.

During Communion, the pastor was always at his most somber and implored us to get our hearts right with God before we ate the crackers and not to partake unless we were truly born again. The whole sanctuary took on a different, more serious tone on those Sunday nights, something akin to what I felt in the cold, piney air of the Catholic Church near my aunt's house.

Communion was our only ritual, and except for the annual missions' conference, the week of evangelistic meetings, Vacation Bible School in the summer, the men's deer-hunting trip in the fall, and the Christmas pageant, it was our only tradition.

Before my family had started celebrating Christmas at my aunt and uncle's house in the Minneapolis suburbs, we'd driven two hours out to rural Bird Island, Minnesota, and slept over at Grammie and Grandpa's, where everything had been pretty much the same every year—Christmas Eve Mass, presents, board games all night, and too much good food on Christmas Day.

So later, when we started going to my aunt and uncle's only on Christmas Day for dinner did I realize what our one family Christmas tradition really was. Not Mass. Not presents from Santa Claus. Not the six-hour game of Monopoly.

The only thing we always did, and always had done, was eat the same Christmas morning breakfast. Christmas morning breakfast was my favorite meal of the year, a cornucopia of a feast, a breakfast that made every Christmas morning a validation of life. Eating that breakfast, I knew how Ebenezer Scrooge had felt when he'd woken up and found out that his nightmare was not real.

We had fresh fruit: pineapple, blueberries, and the only out-of-season strawberries I ate as a child. Thick slices of honey ham and caramel rolls—twin foods whose strong flavors could never overpower each other but only fight for dominance—gooey sugar on chewy ham, salty ham on syrupy sugar. But all these were only sides. Crêpes were the main dish—cream-cheese-filled crêpes drizzled with raspberry sauce and sprinkled with slivered almonds. The crêpes were incredible. And all the more so because we ate them only once a year.

Every year, my dad would take a bite of crêpe and say, "We should have these more often."

But my mom, who'd spent hours over the stove making the pale, paper-thin crêpes, would disagree: "Then they won't be special."

My mom was a lapsed Catholic who still went to Mass a few times a year but not out of any strong religious feeling, only to show my dad that she had her own church and had no desire to attend his. My mom understood the importance of ritual, something my dad could not see. He saw ritual as empty, and yet, he'd be the first to admit that the crêpes were always especially delicious.

Growing up with parents of two different religious persuasions, I paid attention to ritual. Fundamentalist Baptists have no daily rituals—they are not commanded to pray daily or before meals. If you are saved, you should want to do those things and serve the Lord. But when I stopped feeling close to God, I stopped attending church and I fell away from religion after college. Being Baptist wasn't part of my identity. In a way, I felt like I was following in my dad's footsteps—he'd rejected the religion of his parents for something he'd believed to be truer. I did the same.

When I first met my wife, an observant Modern Orthodox Jew, I became aware of how few traditions my family had. Not just religious traditions but family traditions. In Judaism, there is a concept of minhag, the traditions of your family, which may be different from the traditions of the synagogue where you worship. So not only did my wife have a religious tradition that stretched back for thousands of years, but her family also had its own unique minhagim.

When I was born, my family's religious tradition had likely stretched back for hundreds of years—my dad's parents were both German Catholics, my maternal grandmother, an Irish Catholic, and my maternal grandfather, surprisingly enough, a Baptist. But when my dad was born again, we lost that tradition.

Which was why I became especially interested in the crêpes right after I got married. When I asked about their origin, my mom said they'd been eating them for Christmas for at least thirty years, ever since she'd married into the family. My brother, the cook in our family, suggested that they might be a Julia Child recipe from the 1960s.

That made some sense. My grandparents' home had always seemed to me to be stuck in the early sixties—a time that in my mind was the beginning of globalization, a time when Americans were attempting to be more European, more worldly. I imagined Grammie with her hair done up like Jackie O. flipping French pancakes to Bing Crosby singing "Mele Kalikimaka" on the turntable.

The next Christmas, we went over to my aunt's in the afternoon for dinner, and I asked Grammie about the origin of the crêpes.

She told us that her mother had made the crêpes when she was a little girl, but they weren't originally crêpes, but paper-thin German-style pancakes. During the Great Depression, they would make these thin pancakes and eat them with sugar and butter. The cream cheese and raspberry sauce had come later.

I'd known for a long time that, though I could never be a believer, I wanted to raise any children I had with a strong religious tradition. So I'm excited to raise any children I have in my wife's religious tradition.

I'm happy to learn my family has a tradition that I can carry on. I imagine a morning a decade from now, maybe during the last shabbas of the year or maybe the morning after a Passover seder, when my wife, our brood, and I are all sitting down to a breakfast of plump berries, pineapple, crêpes smothered in raspberry sauce, caramel rolls, and kosher vegetarian ham.

SHANE ALAN NOECKER grew up in Minnesota but now lives in Pune, India. He taught high school in California, Louisiana, and Bahrain. His essays have appeared in *South Dakota Review* and *Knock*; his short stories in *Bryant Literary Review*, *Silk Road*, and *Wisconsin Review*. He is the former editor-in-chief of *New Delta Review*.

EATING CRÊPES IN MY MOTHER'S KITCHEN BY LINDSAY TAYLOR

When I was a child, my family never traveled abroad. We never went to art museums or shows at the world-renowned Guthrie Theater. My parents did not attend lectures on Rembrandt or participate in archeological digs. We never wore clothes that cost more than three hours of wages and we never ate at revolving restaurants.

But my mom did make crêpes.

Enter the exotic, the prestigious, the elite. My parents were no longer working-class Midwesterners when the crêpe pan was pulled from the dark back corner of the pots-and-pans cupboard. The sight of the wide silver bottom and the slight tilt of the worn red sides transported us into a higher class. My favorite feature was the engraved words on the bottom of the pan: "Crêpe Pan." I would close my eyes and trace the letters with my finger. No other cookware in the house was so distinguished.

"Do you have my crêpe pan?" my mother asked shortly before my Thanksgiving visit to her Colorado home, years after I was grown and on my own. The pan was one of many items left when she moved several years before. "I miss it," she confessed. "The electric crêpe maker I bought just doesn't turn 'em out like that pan."

So I looked for her crêpe pan and found it in the basement. I wrapped the clunky thing in clothes and positioned it in the middle of my suitcase. Since my visit would include the holiday gift exchange, I bought Mom a crêpe recipe book, *The Ultimate Crêpe Cookbook*, thinking the return of her coveted pan would elicit a resurgence of kitchen creativity.

On my next visit the following year, I saw that new, glossy cookbook on top of her fridge; it was under an orange-and-red, worn book with the simple cursive title: *Crêpes*. It was the cookbook that had come packaged with her pan decades before; the cookbook I knew from my childhood.

I was suddenly transported to my childhood. Mom's crêpe cookbook lay open on the Formica countertop as I wheeled my doll stroller round and round the glass-top kitchen table.

Clink-clink-clink sounds the loose wheel on the front right corner. My doll, Missy, is strapped safely into the checkered seat. I stop my revolutions long enough to see the crêpe pan pulled from the cabinet. Mom had just closed the ironing board with a startling but familiar squeak, placed the iron on the dining room table to cool, and moved her clothes to the closet.

It was Sunday morning. Mom always ironed in the kitchen so that she could watch "Hour of Power" on the little black-and-white TV in the corner of the counter, her pink terrycloth robe secured with a double knot. A small bowl of Cheerios and glass of orange juice rested next to the tube, just a snack to tide her over until the real breakfast.

Now the cookbook claimed her attention. Out came the flour, milk, eggs. I knew to stay close. Imperfect crêpes meant a quick, delicious snack for me. As Mom was no expert in crêpe formation, I'd be nearly full with ripped attempts before settling in at the table with the warm circles rolled around strawberries, topped with a dab of whipped cream. This was no scrambled egg breakfast, as usually happened on Sunday mornings, and it was a far cry from Golden Grahams I could pour for myself on other days. What prompted this rare, alternative breakfast on this morning? Nothing more than my mother's good mood and love of her crêpe pan.

More predictable than the random crêpe breakfast extravaganza was the special occasion dinner. When the special pan and accompanying cookbook appeared in the early evening, I knew guests were expected.

Even though she was less relaxed than on the Sunday morning indulgences, Mom still produced the coveted offering of ripped crêpes. She'd shout my name—or, more often, one of her many nicknames for me—and I'd fetch my appetizer.

The real meal happened in the dining room, at the formal table dressed up in an embroidered white tablecloth and adorned with candlesticks. When the guests arrived, Mom would roll the moist, hot crêpes around the fresh shrimp, crab, and lobster then bury the tubes in creamy white sauce. She always served this meal with a spinach salad; mini croissants (more evidence of our transport to the aristocracy); and chocolate death dessert, a layering of chocolate cake, chocolate mousse, and bright, fresh whipped cream, sprinkled with chocolate shavings. The presentation pulled oohs and ahhs from everyone's mouth. That crêpe pan's magic could always impress guests.

Recently, *Crêpes* arrived in the mail. I called Mom.

"Did you send me your crêpe cookbook?"

"No," she replied, "I found yours at a garage sale. Isn't it a riot? Now we have matching cookbooks." Suddenly, my mind saw the future—when my now-infant son is older, running in and out of the kitchen while I pour the batter. The pan will sizzle as I make my first attempts. Peanut, I'll call when one doesn't turn out just right, I have something for you.

My mind returned to the phone conversation. "Thanks, Mom. I love crêpes." I was touched that she thought of me and excited to try out the recipes from my memories. But, deep down, I knew that my crêpes would never be as good as hers because I didn't have the magical tool with those powerful words etched on the bottom: crêpe pan.

LINDSAY TAYLOR lives in Minneapolis with her husband and two young sons. She usually cooks spaghetti, tacos, and hotdish, but when she's feeling celebratory, she turns to crêpes.

PIPI LA PUSHE BY DON MORREALE

"Whatever you can do, or dream you can, begin it.
Boldness has genius, power, and magic in it."
—Goethe

I could not have been more ill prepared for life in the world. It was the early 1970s, I was in my mid-20's, and up until then I had done nothing more significant with my life than to go to Denver University, where I'd managed, after seven years of noodling around, to earn an undergraduate degree in comparative religions. I didn't know how to drive a car or balance a checkbook. As far as work experience was concerned, I'd pumped gas, packed gloves, washed dishes, jerked sodas, and bused tables—all boring, dead-end jobs that didn't pay squat. To make matters worse, I had developed an attitude, which meant that I would either quit or get fired within six weeks of starting a new job.

I had a pretty good idea of what I *didn't* want to do with my life, which was to move to Costilla County with my girlfriend, whose idea of nirvana was to raise veggies on a hippy commune. What I *did* want to do with my life, however, was a little harder to put my finger on. Whatever it was, it would have to be creative, meaningful, and challenging. It would have to be socially beneficial and, in some arcane way that only a religions major could understand, it would have to take me to a higher spiritual plane.

I kept thinking about Morocco. I'd spent some time in Marrakech while backpacking around the Mediterranean. Marrakech was famous for its central square, Djemaa el-Fna. In the late afternoons the square would fill up with storytellers, dancers, snake charmers, magicians, and guys in hair shirts. Then around dinnertime, the pushcart venders would set up and sell delicious Moroccan food. We'd go every evening, look for a cart that was serving something interesting, and for about fifty cents get a lamb tajine or an elaborate dinner of chicken and couscous.

Djemaa el-Fna was a place of endless fascination for me. Why didn't we have anything like that in Denver, I wondered. If my city ever were to have that sort of vibrant street life, it would be up to guys like me to provide it. Then it struck me, why not set up a pushcart? And sell what? There was already an old guy selling tamales from a cart on Larimer Street. There was another guy selling hot dogs at street fairs on Larimer Square.

No, I wanted something a little more unusual. How about crêpes?

I found a book on crêpe cookery at the library and learned that crêpes were not just a dessert item. You could fill them with chicken, beef, meatballs, asparagus—the possibilities were endless. And since you could roll the fillings into them, they made an ideal street food. And I liked the classiness of the crêpe as well—that French cache.

The idea of selling crêpes from a cart was not universally well received by my friends and family.

"For this I sent you to college?" said my dad.

"Why can't you be normal?" said my mother.

"Small-time capitalist," said my girlfriend, who had studied at Berkeley. She moved out forthwith and headed south and did, in fact, end up raising vegetables in Costilla County.

Now that I knew what I wanted to sell, I needed a pushcart: something with an oven and a couple of ice chests to store the crêpes. And it also had to suggest Paris: an awning, a flower box with geraniums, that sort of thing. I shopped around and discovered there was no such animal out there. If I wanted a quaint little French pushcart, I'd have to build the damned thing myself.

This presented a problem. I didn't know one end of a hammer from another, and besides, I had no tools of my own. I consulted my neighbor Dean, a professional welder and handy man. He offered to let me use his garage and his tools, and every evening when he got home, he'd come out to check on my progress.

The cart became a community project. Dean handled the technical details like the frame, the stove, and the propane tank. My buddy Thaddeus installed the Formica top. A local artist, John Fish, painted the logo. Pam, my roommate's girlfriend, sewed the awning, and my best friend Paul drew up a menu card with the words "Crêpes—65¢" on it. It was a lovely little cart, bright yellow with green trim. I called her "Pipi la Pushe."

City code required that I have a bona fide restaurant kitchen in which to prepare the crêpes, and I found one in an old Denver saloon called "Collins Finer Foods," which was an oxymoron since you couldn't get anything to eat there except for popcorn, Beer Nuts, and pickled eggs. Possibly it was the port on tap that classed up the operation. The bartenders wore their aprons long, like old-time saloon keepers, and the clientele were a bouillabaisse of cowboys, Indians, poets, jazz musicians, bikers, ex-cons, pensioners, winos, evangelicals, and drag queens, all convivially drinking themselves to death. The smell of stale beer, cigarettes, and Pine Sol hovered over the booths like swamp gas.

The kitchen, however, was just perfect for my needs. It came equipped with an old-fashioned six-burner stove, a stainless-steel work table, a pot-washing sink, and a deli-style refrigerator with locks on the doors. The rent was more than fair. I got it for fifty bucks a month.

On the eve of Pipi's *vernissage*, I stayed at the kitchen late into the night, cooking my first batch of crêpes. Setting my four crêpe pans to heat on the big restaurant stove, I threw in some butter, ladled in the batter, and timed the cooking so that each pancake finished just ahead of the next in one continuous flow. Soon I had a pile of sixty golden crêpes, stacked in a warming pan, pretty as you please.

Next I turned my attention to the fillings. For the grand opening I wanted something really elegant, so I decided on boeuf bourguignon and Mediterranean chicken with olives and capers for the dinner entrées, and bananas in sour cream and apple slices sautéed in cinnamon for the desserts. I spooned the fillings into the crêpes and wrapped them in aluminum foil and put them away in the refrigerator.

I was up at six the next morning, bleary-eyed but excited. I drove to my storage space, retrieved the cart, and pushed it the two blocks to the kitchen on wheels that seemed a little shaky to me. They were heavy-duty bicycle wheels with balloon tires, recommended by the guys at House of Wheels.

"They'll be fine," they said. "No problem."

But I was worried they might not be able to take the strain of daily use. It seems incredible to me now, but I was heading into opening day without having road-tested the equipment.

I left the cart at the side door while I ran into the kitchen to get my supplies. I should have known better, because there were a couple of rough-looking characters leaning against the wall outside, and in the two minutes I was inside, they jumped on the cart and rode it down the sidewalk until the wheels gave out and the cart tipped over. They were laughing and hooting when I came out. I saw a cop car and waved it down. The drunks took off running.

"What seems to be the trouble, son?" asked the cop.

"Some bums just jumped my cart and busted the wheels. That's them right there!"

"Can you give me a description?"

"Description? You don't need a description, man. There they are!"

"Any witnesses?"

"Those are the guys, I'm telling you!"

"But did you actually see them do it?"

"Well, no, not exactly, but ..."

He put away his notebook. "Can't make an arrest without a witness," he said, getting back into his cruiser.

Later that day, I sat in a booth with my friend Patsy, and we kicked it around over a couple of boilermakers. Patsy was teaching philosophy at Denver University when I first met her, and over the years she'd become a friend and confidant.

"You seem pretty down," she said.

"I feel like just blowing it off." I downed the whisky and chased it with a swig of beer. "I've been looking at the world through rose-colored glasses, Patsy. I mean, you go along figuring the cops are there to protect you, but they're not. They don't give a damn. They're just covering their asses."

"Welcome to the real world," she said.

"You can't assume the universe is watching over you," I said.

"No. You can't. But you can't assume the universe is out to get you, either. It's wise to lock your stuff down, but you can also end up armor-plating your heart to the extent that you miss out on all the good things life has to offer."

"The way I see it, she said, holding her palms upward in imitation of a scale, "it's a balancing act. Self-preservation on the one hand; openness and trust on the other."

"You mean like, 'Trust in God, but keep your camel tied'?" I said.

"Something like that," she said.

The guys at House of Wheels replaced the bicycle tires with "wino resistant" motorcycle wheels, and the following day I rolled the cart out into the sunshine for another shot at a grand opening. Donning chef's hat and apron, I filled the two ice chests with crêpes and pushed the cart the six blocks to the state Capitol Building. I opened the awning; set out the menu card, the napkin dispenser, and the condiments; unscrewed the valve on the propane tank; and lit the oven. Pipi la Pushe was open for business.

It took some time for people to work up the courage to sample my wares. This was 1974, remember, and the standard opinion about Denver, even among those of us who lived there and loved it, was that it was a cow town—"Omaha with mountains"—which, to be honest, was not far from the truth. Most people in the Mile High City couldn't tell a crêpe from a baseball bat, and the notion of eating something off a pushcart was utterly foreign. So, I had to educate my public on the glories of the French flapjack.

"What are them creepies you're sellin' there, son?" asks the man in the cowboy hat.

"Crêpes," I say.

"Craps? What's that?"

"Sort of like a French burrito."

"What's in 'em?"

"Today we have boeuf bourguignon and Mediterranean chicken."

"Buff. That the same as beef?"

"Yes, sir. Like to try one?"

"Oh, hell, why not? Gimme one of them there beef craps."

"Crêpes."

"Like I said, son."

I remove a piping-hot, foil-wrapped crêpe from the oven, hand it over, and await the verdict.

"Ain't half bad, son. Ain't half bad a-tall. Gimme another'n."

I probably could have gotten more than the piddling sixty-five cents I was charging, but I was naïve and eager to please and believed that street food should be both cheap and tasty, but above all cheap.

The business grew slowly, and in a couple of months I had a regular little clientele: legislators from the Capitol Building; commuters waiting for the bus; office workers on their lunch breaks; Jerry, from Jerry's Used Books across the street; the guys from the House of Wheels; the occasional European tourist, delighted by this unexpected reminder of home on the streets of Denver. Then a reporter from the *Denver Post* showed up.

"So, how did you get started in the pushcart business?" she asked, opening her notebook.

"Wait. First, try one," I said, handing her a crêpe filled with spinach, mushrooms, and Gruyere.

"Mmmm," she said.

"Not bad, eh?"

"Delicious."

"I used to live in Paris," I said. "That's where I first learned about crêpes. That's also where I met Madame Pipi."

"Madame Pipi?"

"Pipi la Pushe."

"She was a real person?"

"Oh, yes," I said. "Paris streetwalker. The proverbial whore with a heart of gold. Took me in when I was down and out and living on the streets. Let me crash in her pad on the Rue de Vallé. Cooked the best crêpes I ever ate. Taught me how to make 'em. Even gave me the start-up money. So, of course I had to name the business after her."

"Quite a story," said the reporter, closing her notebook. I could see the wheels turning as she framed her lead.

For the record, I don't know exactly where I got the name "Pipi la Pushe." It just sort of popped into my head one day, as did the whopper about "Pipi" being a real Paris hooker. But it was a catchy name, and people remembered it.

The *Post* ran the story verbatim, a half page of text and a page and a half of pictures, and the next day there was a line a block long waiting to take the plunge. Soon invitations began pouring in to cater parties and to set up my cart at street fairs like the Oktoberfest in Denver's Larimer Square where we rechristened the product *Phannekuchin*, which is German for "pancake."

I worked my ass off that fall, though I never did figure out how much I was paying myself on an hourly basis. In a way, it didn't matter because something bigger was happening in my life as a result of the pushcart experience. I went from being a rather tentative and geeky religious studies major to a confident and self-reliant actor in the world. There was also a kind of spiritual fulfillment in the effort we were making. By now I had three helpers working for me in the kitchen, trying to keep up with the demand.

One Saturday morning, the four of us were scrambling to get ready for Oktoberfest. I was at the stove cooking pancakes while my helpers had stationed themselves around the big stainless-steel work table and were filling and wrapping crêpes in assembly-line fashion.

At one point I realized that someone was tapping me on the shoulder, and a voice was calling my name.

"Don. Don? Don!!!" I looked up. "Do you realize I've been trying to get your attention for the past five minutes?"

It was my helper, Tina. My concentration had been so riveted that I hadn't even heard her. I was in the Pancake Zone, and it had taken a shout and a nudge to pull me out of it.

Today, with years of meditation experience under my belt, I know this to have been what Zennists call "Sunyata" or Emptiness—a state of absorption so profound that the sense of self disappears.

The Chinese poet Li Po put it this way:

> We sit together
> the mountain and me,
> 'til only the mountain remains.

Flipping flapjacks as peak experience—now there's something they didn't teach us in the Department of Religion.

When winter came, I put the cart in storage and contemplated my next move. I was young and restless and had lots of ideas floating around in my head for things I wanted to do—like hitchhike to India, for example. I sold the cart to a guy in Boulder who reopened it as "Goldstein's Burritos" and used the money to finance the trip to India.

But that, as they say, is a whole other story.

DON MORREALE is the author of *Buddhist America: Centers, Retreats, and Practices* and *The Complete Guide to Buddhist America*. He lives in Denver, Colorado, and travels and lectures worldwide.

CRÊPE SUCRÉ BY MELISSA DOFFING

It was my first night in Paris. Candles flickered and the dark air of the café was filled with smoke and jazz. Everyone was older than me. The lone freshman among juniors and seniors, I had felt one step behind since I arrived in the City of Lights. During our first class on Expatriate Literature, I got lost somewhere between the French Feminists and Deconstruction. Our introductory tour of Paris was a blur—Sacré Coeur, the Champs-Élysées, Luxembourg Gardens, Eiffel Tower, Notre Dame, the Seine, the Louvre—they all melded together in my mind, shades of black and gray. I was on sensory overload and had no idea how I would navigate such a huge city on my own for the next three weeks.

I focused intently on the jazz, my glass of red wine, the French around me with its unfamiliar sounds both alluring and harsh. I couldn't help feeling that my nineteen-year-old attempt at something bold and adventurous was a big mistake.

But as the days passed, I eased into the study abroad experience. I explored the city with my fellow classmates, carefully read the assignments, and began to speak both literary theory and French. I learned the differences between the French and American Feminists and the relationship between Deconstruction in the literary world and the larger arts community. I read Gertrude Stein, Ernest Hemingway, and F. Scott Fitzgerald, developing a kinship to those famous Americans living in Paris. As I walked the same narrow streets that had been their muse, their protection, and their *raison d'être*, I soaked in the promise of Paris. And even though I'd never studied French, I found I could read a menu even if I couldn't pronounce the words. Armed with my new Parisian scarf and a few useful phrases, I became a Francophile within days. And it wasn't just Paris.

Despite my initial naïveté, I felt a growing sense of my independent self in Paris. It began in earnest the day I decided to venture out alone into my temporary neighborhood. I pulled on my gray wool coat, tied a scarf smartly around my neck in the French style, and walked confidently out the front doors of Hotel Trianon Rive Gauche into the Latin Quarter.

Turning onto Boulevard St. Michel, I walked past a patisserie where scrumptious desserts lined the window and the smell of croissants wafted out the door. I passed a lingerie boutique with delectable desserts of a different kind displayed suggestively on the mannequins. Further up the street was a small market whose entrance was framed with baskets of fresh fruit and flowers. The Café Le Luxembourg was filled with Parisians leisurely sipping *café crème* and reading worn copies of *Madame Bovary* or the latest French novel. The atrium faced the Luxembourg Gardens where bare, black branches entwined—stark and half frozen—with the January sun.

And then I was suddenly engulfed in a smell so warm and sweet that I had to stop. A petite stand was tucked under the awning of a confectionary shop just a few feet away, and the aroma drew me in. It was a crêpe stand.

During our first day in Paris, we had been warned by the tour director about the risks of eating street food. I looked from the menu to the batter bubbling on the griddle and took the first of many steps towards independence.

"*Bonjour, Mademoiselle,*" the man behind the griddle greeted me.

"*Crêpe sucré,*" I immediately responded, surprising myself with the clarity with in which the words flew out of my mouth. I sounded, well, French.

The man nodded without any recognition of the significance of the moment we were sharing. He poured enough batter to thinly coat the large, round griddle. It sizzled as it started to steam and curl in the crisp

January air. He quickly flipped the crêpe, slathered it with butter and sprinkled it with sugar. And with three swift movements of his spatula, the crêpe was no longer a thin pancake on the griddle, but a smooth triangular pastry in a paper liner. I exchanged a handful of francs for my treat. We both smiled as I turned to walk away.

Across the street was one of the many entrances to the Luxembourg Gardens. I dodged Renaults and Volkswagens as I crossed the street to claim my place on a bench just on the edge of the garden and breathe in the perfect bouquet of the crêpe, the foliage, and the city.

People hustled by, hunched against the brisk wind while I listened to the smooth, rhythmic cadence of the French language around me. I bit into my crêpe, letting the butter and sugar melt on my tongue and found that the language that had seemed so foreign a few weeks ago was now soothing and familiar. This was what being independent was about. Letting the sweet taste of a new experience overwhelm your senses and surround you. Simultaneously losing and finding yourself in a moment, in a crêpe, in a garden, while enjoying each luscious bite.

MELISSA DOFFING has published a broad range of work. Recent publication credits include creative nonfiction in *Salome Magazine*, articles in *Savvy Women's Magazine,* and book reviews in *Women Writers: A Zine*. She is currently working on her first novel, *Chasing Fireflies*.

THE NUNS OF BERLAYMONT BY LUCY FERRISS

It strains my imagination to remember the tastes of 1969. I don't mean taste in cars (fins, muscles) or clothes (minis, paper dresses), but tastes. Fish sticks. Shepherd's pie with instant mashed potatoes. Chipped beef. Iceberg lettuce. Hi Hos. I grew up in St. Louis. We adhered closely to the Four Food Groups: Dairy, Meat, Starch, and Vegetables or Fruit. I didn't much like eating, and it surprised me that anyone had to diet—not because I didn't understand about calories, but because I couldn't see where a person would ingest more of this stuff than necessary to stay alive. My mother was considered a good cook, especially her casseroles. I was not a good cook and never sought to be one.

I was, however, good at French. When a high school exchange program to French-speaking Belgium came across my parents' horizon, they floated it by me. I could scarcely locate Belgium on a map, but as soon as I saw the program description, I wanted to go. It was far, far away from St. Louis and in a boarding school where I would speak French all day, every day. French cheered me up. I had only to mouth *"mon semblable, mon frère"* to be in a better mood. So off I went, at fifteen, for a semester at the Monastère de Berlaymont in Waterloo, walking distance from where Napoleon met his downfall.

Initially, there were five girls in the exchange group. Within a fortnight, however, the coolest and meanest of us had grown homesick, leaving three: Mary, Molly, and me. We had our own wing of the dormitory and our own proctor. Assigned to watch over us by the exchange program, Ruth was a former junior high math teacher with a weakness for sherry, who had fallen in love with a German graduate student and seized this job to chase him back to Dortmund. At first, she slipped away during the week to see her boyfriend, but when he broke up with her, she took to drinking in her room, leaving us mostly on our own.

The school was run by the nuns of Berlaymont, who lived in their own residence across the back courtyard. Only a few of them taught classes, but they monitored the hallways and dished up food at lunch and dinner, and in the evenings a handful occupied a corner of the top floor of the dorm, which was reserved for recreation. There, while we schoolgirls played ping-pong or gathered in groups to gossip, they took up a corner with a nightly canasta game in which francs traveled from one nun's pocket to another's.

At home, we were good Midwestern Protestants. Except for Sally Fields on TV, flying about in her white habit, nuns frightened me. At lunch during my first week at the boarding school, the dessert line featured a creamy white pudding. I accepted my bowl from the first black-cloaked lady who served it up and moved down the line to the next, who was—to my horror—dishing out spoonfuls of white sugar. "*Un, deux, ou trois?*" this nun gently asked me.

I shook my head. Sugar in pudding! I was trying to expand my tastes—I drank the small beer they served at meals, glubbed down mussels, let my tongue slip over the surface of stinky cheeses. Strange as it all was, the tastes so far beat anything I'd yet experienced in St. Louis. Mary, especially, had taken to the fat croissants and sweet creamy butter, and we could tell that soon she would need a refitting of her navy-blue school uniform. But sugar on pudding—now there was a bar I could not cross. "*Non, merci,*" I told the little nun.

She frowned. "*Un, tu veux?*" she tried again, the teaspoon holding its tiny hillock of crystals, reaching shakily toward my bowl.

"*Non, non,*" I said. I backed away. "*Rien, merci!*"

She shook her covered head, perplexed at the American who refused sugar, and turned to the next girl, who took three spoonfuls. I returned to my seat at the long table where I had begun to make a few friends among my Belgian schoolmates. While they stirred in their sugar, I took a bite of the pudding and recoiled. Why, it tasted like buttermilk! Sour and tangy, it was not pudding at all. The girl across from me touched my hand and asked in French what the matter was.

"What is this stuff?" I whispered.

"Why, it's yogurt," she said. "Don't you like it?"

Yogurt. I had never heard of it. The next time the dessert was served, I took two teaspoonfuls from the sugar-ladling nun, who smiled primly at my education in taste. At my seat, I stirred the sugar in like the others, then tasted a miracle of sharp, yeasty creaminess interrupted by the crunch of the grains and the milky syrup they had started to form.

From then on, I tasted everything and scrupulously copied Belgian behavior in food. I slathered my French fries with mayonnaise and ate them with knife and fork. I consumed raw "steak *Américain*." I ate Belgian waffles, hot and crunchy from the waxed paper, without mentioning maple syrup. Taste buds I never knew I possessed flowered in my mouth.

In the evenings, I started playing canasta. If there was one talent I could import from the middle of the United States, it was counting cards. My mother, like all mothers, had a weekly bridge game, and on rainy summer afternoons our family dealt everything from hearts to Russian bank. Canasta was up my alley, and it required less verbal acumen than gossiping with the Berlaymont girls. Much as I still loved French, by evening my brain felt fried by language. So while the now-plump Mary giggled in a corner, and Molly the athlete brandished a ping-pong paddle, I matched wits with the nuns.

Mostly they took my francs, but once or twice I had a good night. I became less afraid of them and started to notice the faces matted in white and framed in black. Some were old and soft, others young and severe. I learned three of their names: Annette, Marie-Christine, Genevieve.

One night, Marie-Christine—who was the oldest and wore the heaviest cross around her neck—asked if my friends and Ruth and I would care to come to their apartment and enjoy an evening of crêpes.

Crêpes. Back in my room, I looked it up in my French-English dictionary. "Pancakes." For dinner? Would there be maple syrup as there never was for the waffles? I told Ruth about the invitation.

"Oh, we must go," she said, smiling weakly. "It would be rude to refuse. They drink good wine, those nuns."

Mary and Molly were not so enthusiastic, but when I told them there were pancakes to be had, they perked up. We three had adjusted to Belgium and to each other. Molly had started playing on Berlaymont's fencing team and had been tapped to advise its fledgling field hockey team on the strategies of this American sport. Mary babbled bad French like a brook and indulged herself in everything—sweets, clothes, new friends. I had a bit part in the school's production of *Phèdre*—and of course, I had the nuns. Next Wednesday, Ruth signed us out of the refectory. Still in our uniforms, my right skirt pocket bulging with one-franc pieces, the four of us tiptoed rather nervously across the courtyard.

Marie-Christine's apartment was small, dark, crowded with furniture and small *objets d'art* from what she referred to as her "adventure years." It was also bustling, my three canasta buddies laying a table with linen and china, Jacques Brel on the phonograph. *"Mon dieu!"* I exclaimed when Annette opened the door. There was her whole face, her whole head, dark brown hair swept back into a tight bun, slender neck descending to a plain blue sweater. None of them wore a habit. Marie-Christine herself looked like my maternal grandmother, heavy-armed and thick-ankled beneath her skirt.

"We needn't wear the habit in our private quarters," explained Genevieve, who looked even younger than in her robe and more shy than severe.

"A good thing, too," said Marie-Christine. "I'd be sweating in here!"

It was warm, the air redolent of eggs, cheese, ham, and the bitter scent of cooked endive. We shucked our jackets. Ruth began poking about—rudely, I thought—while Mary answered Annette's questions with eager, mangled sentences. ("Where do you live, in America?" "I have my house from Pennsylvania, that is a state very not so small, my brothers and mother there, but my father he little the crying likes—I mean rain, he is not the rain—but I have a ceiling—I mean floor— ")

Genevieve gave us all glasses, not of wine, but of cider—different from the cider at home, tickling my tongue and leaving a funny aftertaste. I thought Ruth would want to leave when she saw there was no booze, but she seemed to like the cider well enough. Sipping, I wandered into the kitchen where Marie-Christine was chopping vegetables and bits of meat while Annette whisked a bowl of what looked like brownish egg nog. I guessed we weren't having pancakes after all.

"Can I help?" I asked.

Annette grinned. She was a pretty woman, out of her habit. "Have you made crêpes?"

"No—I mean, yes. American crêpes. But we only have them for breakfast."

"Crêpes for breakfast!" She giggled. "Well, you may watch. Marie-Christine, she is the queen of crêpes. Did you know, she used to own a restaurant?"

Marie-Christine shot her a look, but Annette only rolled her eyes. I didn't know what I was allowed to ask—where the restaurant had been, what had happened to it, had she been married? While I stood dumb, Marie-Christine handed me a cutting board and a pile of crisp cooked bacon. "Chop it very fine," she advised.

While I found a corner of the counter, Marie-Christine examined the egg nog and pronounced it ready. Then she set a round, flat skillet on the stove, lit the gas, and dropped a tablespoon of butter on the skillet. Just as it began to smoke, she ladled a scoop of the egg nog into the middle and swished it around. Quickly it formed tiny bubbles. She loosened one edge and then, suddenly, with a dexterity that her thick arms belied, flipped the thing into the air and caught the other side on the skillet. "Endive," she demanded from Annette, "and ham."

These things, along with a handful of grated cheese, she sprinkled in the center of the skillet. With another set of quick motions—forward, up, back, forward, up—she rolled the flat thing around its contents. My mouth watered. "What is that?"

Annette put her thin hand on my shoulder. "Why, my little *chou*," she said, "that is a crêpe."

"Galette," corrected Marie-Christine, rolling the concoction onto a plate and setting it in the oven. Immediately she began buttering the skillet anew.

"Galette," Annette explained, "is what we call the salty crêpes. The sweet ones we will have for dessert."

In a short time, Marie-Christine had prepared a dozen of these heavenly concoctions—filled not just with the endive-ham combination, but with fried egg and spinach, bacon and cheese, cheese alone. When we had a stack, I was instructed to gather the group, and we took our places around the nuns' cramped table.

"What are those?" said Ruth, rather loudly. She had been making a dent in the cider, which I managed to figure for something more lethal than the stuff we squeezed from apples in Missouri.

"Galettes," I said, as if this were a term everyone knew. On either side of me, the nuns bowed their heads.

"*Seigneur,*" intoned Annette, and for a minute, as she said grace, I remembered that these were nuns. Then she finished, we dug in. What lightness! What crisp lace at the edges, what cheese melting within! Even the egg, a plain fried egg wrapped in its thin blanket, tasted like food truly blessed. Soon we had finished the pile, and Marie-Christine had quietly slipped away to the kitchen to prepare seconds.

"Afterwards," said Annette, her eyes twinkling as she poured more cider into my mug, "Canasta."

By the second round, Ruth had gone a little glazed-eyed, and Mary's French had descended into a Dadaist jumble. Genevieve was explaining the rules of canasta to Molly, whose normal reticence had loosened under the influence of the cider, and I was exploring the taste the endive left along the side of my tongue. "Come help me," Marie-Christine said, tapping my shoulder as she headed back into the kitchen.

Annette was already whisking another bowl of egg nog, this one more lemony than before. Lined up on the little counter were bowls of powdered sugar, jam, *crème fraiche*, and sliced poached pear. These, I understood, were the real crêpes, the dessert version. By now, the little apartment was steamy. We had all removed our sweaters; our faces glowed. Marie-Christine instructed me to carry the bowls to the table. When I returned, she was tossing and folding a crêpe, its edges golden brown, and tipping it onto a plate.

"Now, you," she said as I stood by.

"Me?"

"You make the crêpe. Here we go." She ladled the batter onto the griddle and turned the handle toward me. I gripped it with both hands.

On the counter lay a table knife for loosening the edge, but no spatula was in sight. "Quickly, quickly!" said Marie-Christine. She planted herself behind me and reached around, her massive belly pressing against my back, to put her thick, lined hands over mine. Together we swirled the thin pancake around the skillet. Then, my hands trapped beneath Marie-Christine's, we threw the crêpe up and—magically—shoved the heavy skillet forward to catch it.

"Wow," I said.

"*Ah, oui*. Wow," said Marie-Christine. She took over—flipping, folding, tipping onto the plate. "Now, you alone. *Toute seule*."

I was terrified. I dropped butter onto the skillet, let it bubble, ladled the lemony batter, swirled. Immediately the little bubbles and holes formed. I loosened the edge. I held my breath and gripped the handle with both hands. I gave a jerk. Up flew the crêpe—up, up, higher than Marie-Christine's had gone, up almost to the speckled ceiling. Then down and whoosh, onto the skillet. "I did it!" I cried.

"Good girl."

I flipped and folded, folded again, tipped. Oh, they were lovely. As I carried the laden plate out to the little dining room, Annette followed. She had been heating something up on the other burner of the stove, a warm, spicy-smelling liquid. As I set the plate down in the center of the cleared table, she poured the liquid over the pile and lit a match. The whole thing flared—blue at the edges, gold in the center. A collective sigh went around the table.

"*C'est magnifique*," said Mary—the first flawless thing she had uttered since we arrived in Belgium. I was transfixed by the colored fire, which flickered, died away, and left behind a smell of longing and desire. Genevieve distributed the crêpes. I ate mine with pears and a dollop of crème fraiche.

Though surely the flame had burned away the alcohol in what I learned was brandy, I felt drunk, giddy on crêpes and cider and the close air of the nuns' apartment, the happiness of these women who had given their lives to God and cards and good food.

Ruth had passed out in the lone armchair in the corner of the room. Mary's face was pink with warmth and sugar. Molly had begun to babble a bit, in better French than I knew she possessed. At last Marie-Christine placed her heavy hands palm down on the table.

"Now," she said, "we clear. And then we play."

The nuns exchanged glances. Genevieve gathered our plates. Annette jumped up to fetch the deck of cards. I felt the weight of the francs in my skirt pocket. They were a price, I knew, I would be glad to pay.

LUCY FERRISS is the author of six published books of fiction, most recently *Nerves of the Heart* (U. Tennessee, 2002) and the memoir *Unveiling the Prophet* (U. Missouri, 2005). Her novel *The Woman Who Bought the Sky* will be published by Tor Books in 2011. Her short fiction and essays have been published widely, and she contributes occasionally to the *New York Times*. She is the writer-in-residence at Trinity College in Connecticut.

-Photo by Kurt Koefod

ABOUT THE EDITORS

Melissa Doffing and Susan Koefod live and write near the Twin Cities in Minnesota. They were drawn together for this anthology by a hunger for good writing and crêpes. Doffing enjoys reading and writing in a variety of genres and is currently trying her hand at fiction. Koefod works during the day as a business writer and moonlights as a poet and novelist. Their favorite crêpes are crêpe sucré and the Russian blini with caviar.

PUBLICATION CREDITS

Grateful acknowledgement is made to the authors for their permission to use their material in this collection. We also acknowledge the following publications:

Breakfast in Helsinki was first published in the online journal *Literary Bohemian* in Issue 5, June 2009.

One Tradition first appeared in print in the 2010 edition of *Two Review: A Journal of International Poetry & Creative Nonfiction.*

A Bunch of the Boys Were Whooping It Up first appeared online in *On the Table: the curious home of food writer & dilettante Gary Allen* on July 2, 2010.

An excerpt from *Spanish Pancakes* by Erica Rivera appears in her memoir, *Insatiable: A Young Mother's Struggle with Anorexia* published by Berkley Books on October 6, 2009. Reprinted with permission.